CONTENTS

GRADE 2

ISBN: 978-1-927042-11-3

1 Numbers to 100

Write the numbers in words.

① 9 _____

② 13 _____

③ 17 _____

④ 15 _____

⑤ 20 _____

Fill in the missing numbers.

⑥ 66 67 ___ 69 ___ ___ 72

⑦ 88 87 ___ 85 ___ ___ 82

⑧ 39 ___ 41 ___ 43 44 ___

⑨ 92 ___ 90 ___ 88 87 ___

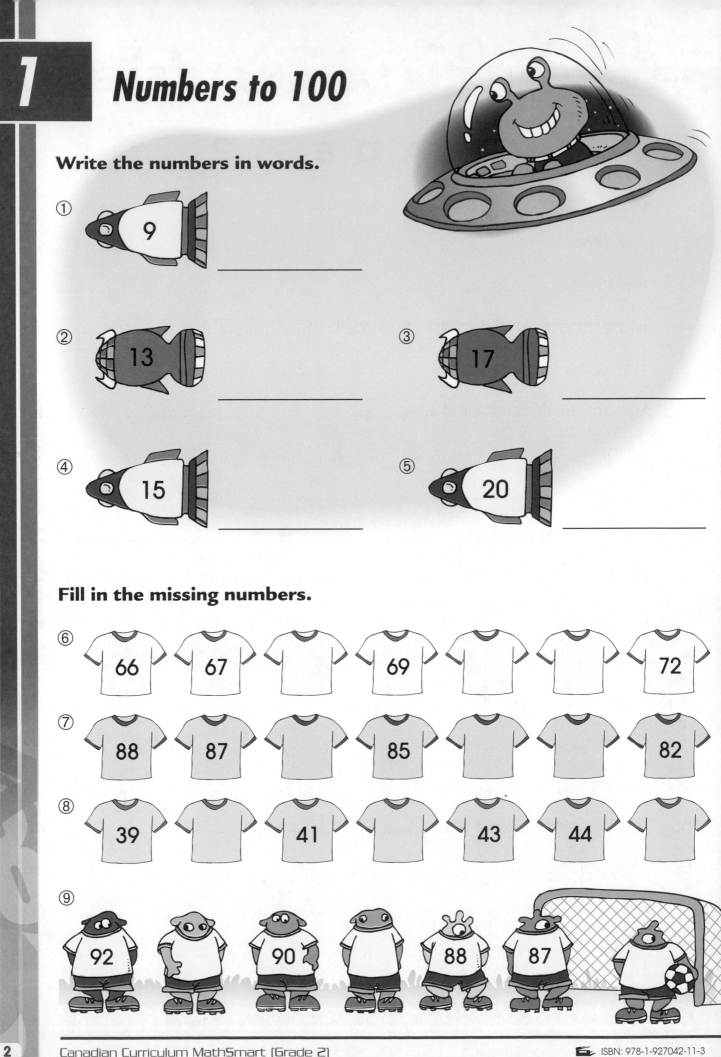

ISBN: 978-1-927042-11-3

Count the stars. Write the numbers.

⑩ Count by 2's.

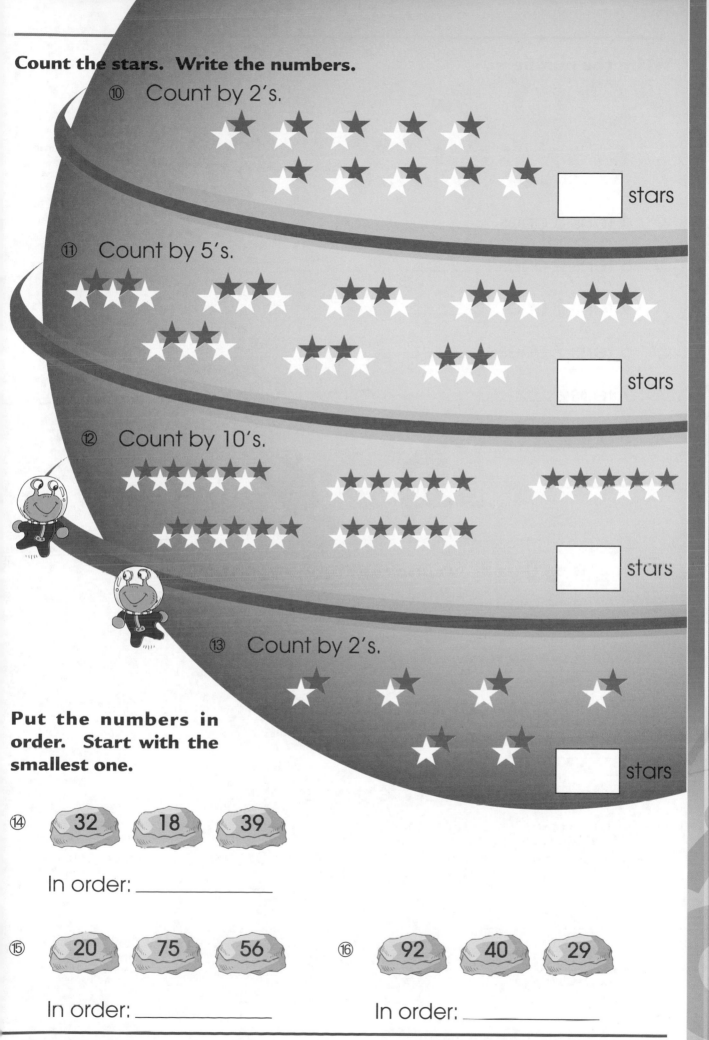

☐ stars

⑪ Count by 5's.

☐ stars

⑫ Count by 10's.

☐ stars

⑬ Count by 2's.

Put the numbers in order. Start with the smallest one.

☐ stars

⑭ 32   18   39

In order: _____

⑮ 20   75   56

In order: _____

⑯ 92   40   29

In order: _____

ISBN: 978-1-927042-11-3

Write the numbers.

⑰ 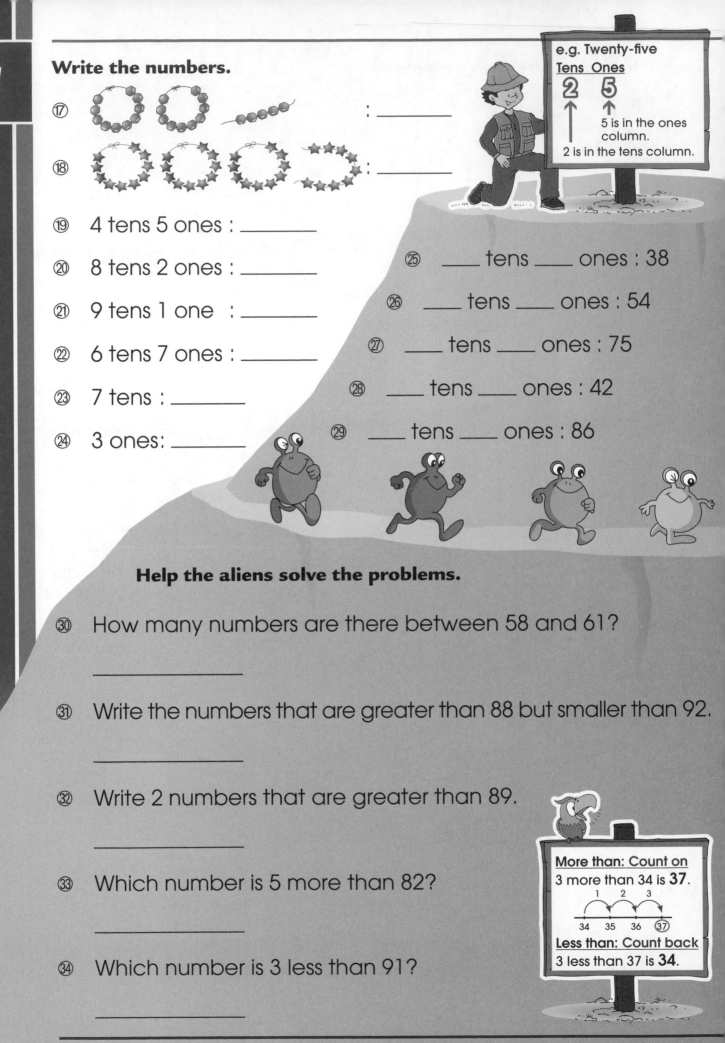 : _____

⑱ : _____

e.g. Twenty-five
Tens Ones
2 5

↑ ↑
5 is in the ones column.
2 is in the tens column.

⑲ 4 tens 5 ones : _____

⑳ 8 tens 2 ones : _____

㉑ 9 tens 1 one : _____

㉒ 6 tens 7 ones : _____

㉓ 7 tens : _____

㉔ 3 ones: _____

㉕ ___ tens ___ ones : 38

㉖ ___ tens ___ ones : 54

㉗ ___ tens ___ ones : 75

㉘ ___ tens ___ ones : 42

㉙ ___ tens ___ ones : 86

Help the aliens solve the problems.

㉚ How many numbers are there between 58 and 61?

_____

㉛ Write the numbers that are greater than 88 but smaller than 92.

_____

㉜ Write 2 numbers that are greater than 89.

_____

㉝ Which number is 5 more than 82?

_____

㉞ Which number is 3 less than 91?

_____

More than: Count on
3 more than 34 is **37**.

    1   2   3
34 35 36 (37)

Less than: Count back
3 less than 37 is **34**.

Canadian Curriculum MathSmart (Grade 2)   ISBN: 978-1-927042-11-3

Fill in the missing ordinal numbers and complete the sentences.

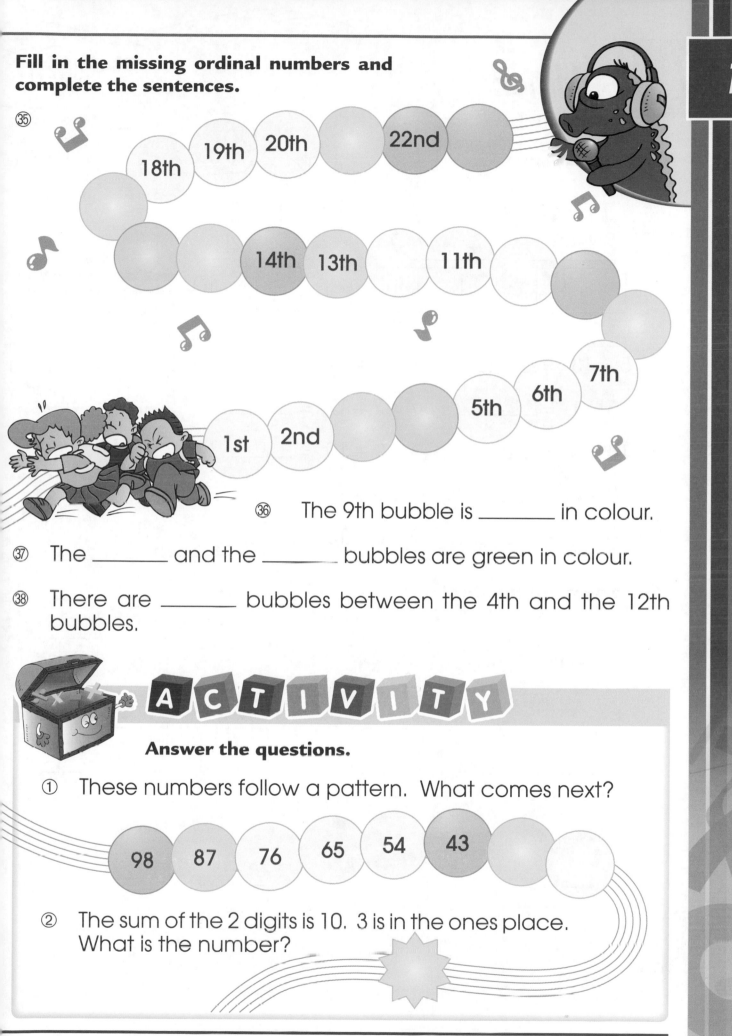

㉟

18th 19th 20th 22nd

14th 13th 11th

7th
6th
5th

1st 2nd

㊱ The 9th bubble is _____ in colour.

㊲ The _____ and the _____ bubbles are green in colour.

㊳ There are _____ bubbles between the 4th and the 12th bubbles.

ACTIVITY

Answer the questions.

① These numbers follow a pattern. What comes next?

98 87 76 65 54 43

② The sum of the 2 digits is 10. 3 is in the ones place. What is the number?

ISBN: 978-1-927042-11-3

Canadian Curriculum MathSmart (Grade 2)

Addition

Do the addition.

①
$$\begin{array}{r} 1\ 4 \\ +\quad 3 \\ \hline \end{array}$$

②
$$\begin{array}{r} 1\ 1 \\ +\quad 7 \\ \hline \end{array}$$

③
$$\begin{array}{r} 1\ 2 \\ +\quad 4 \\ \hline \end{array}$$

> Remember to align the numbers on the right.
>
> $$\begin{array}{r} 12 \\ +\ 3 \\ \hline 15 \end{array} \text{✗} \qquad \begin{array}{r} 12 \\ +\ 3 \\ \hline 15 \end{array} \text{✔}$$

④ 5 + 13 = _____

⑤ 6 + 12 = _____

⑥ 15 + 1 = _____

⑦ 2 + 17 = _____

⑧ 14 + 5 = _____

⑨ 9 + 10 = _____

⑩ 10 + 4 = _____

⑪ 5 + 11 = _____

⑫ 16 + 1 = _____

⑬ 6 + 13 = _____

Count and find the totals.

⑭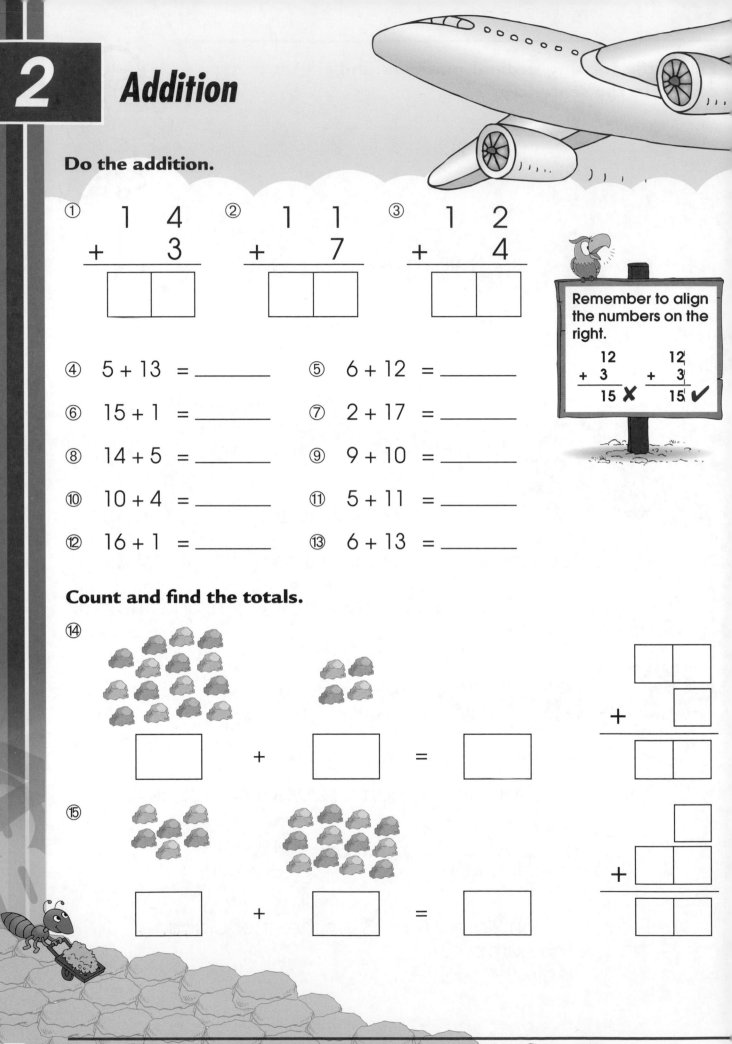

⬜ + ⬜ = ⬜

⑮

⬜ + ⬜ = ⬜

ISBN: 978-1-927042-11-3

Count the pears. Write the numbers in the boxes.

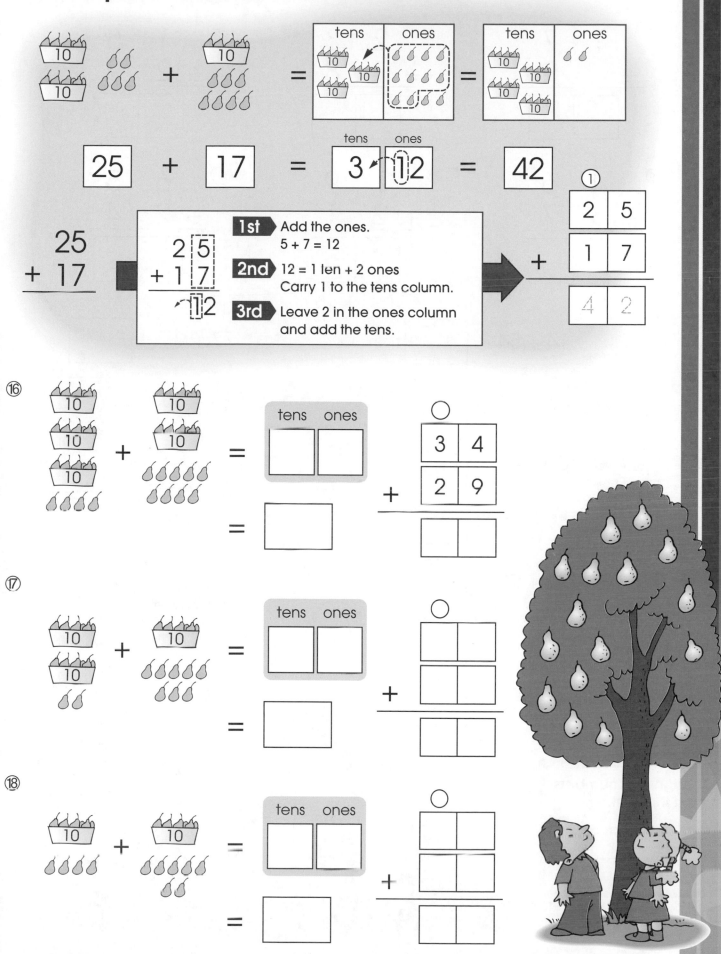

$$25 + 17 = 3\ 12 = 42$$

tens	ones

①

2	5
1	7
4	2

$$25 + 17$$

	2	5
+	1	7
	1	2

1st Add the ones.
5 + 7 = 12

2nd 12 = 1 ten + 2 ones
Carry 1 to the tens column.

3rd Leave 2 in the ones column
and add the tens.

⑯

tens	ones

3	4
2	9

⑰

tens	ones

⑱

tens	ones

ISBN: 978-1-927042-11-3

2

Find the answers.

⑲
```
  1 7
+   9
```

⑳
```
  2 3
+ 1 8
```

㉑
```
  1 5
+ 2 9
```

㉒
```
  4 6
+ 3 7
```

㉓
```
  1 9
+ 2 1
```

㉔
```
  6 5
+ 2 4
```

㉕ 14 + 54 =

㉖ 77 + 9 =

㉗ 69 + 11 =

㉘ 25 + 55 =

㉙ 8 + 44 =

㉚ 57 + 16 =

㉛ 39 + 12 =

㉜ 16 + 38 =

㉝ 47 + 29 =

㉞ 27 + 27 =

㉟ 52 + 18 =

Align the numbers on the right.
```
  32        32
+ 19      + 19
  51 ✗     51 ✔
```

Remember to carry groups of 10 from the ones column to the tens column.

Canadian Curriculum MathSmart (Grade 2)

ISBN: 978-1-927042-11-3

Solve the problems.

㊱ There are 22  and 19 on the beach. How many children are there in all?

[ ] + [ ] = [ ]   [ ] children

㊲ Peter makes 48 on the sand and Ruby makes 38. How many footprints do the children make in all?

[ ] + [ ] = [ ]

[ ] footprints

㊳ Judy collects 17 . Tommy collects 16. How many shells do they collect in all?

[ ] + [ ] = [ ]   [ ] shells

ACTIVITY

Peter is on the boat with the greatest sum. Check ✔ the correct boat.

A $64 + 28$

B $19 + 77$

C $56 + 34$

D $46 + 35$

3 Subtraction

How many flowers are left?

①

$$\boxed{} - \boxed{} = \boxed{}$$

②

$$\boxed{} - \boxed{} = \boxed{}$$

$$\begin{array}{r} 13 \\ -\ 7 \end{array} \longrightarrow \begin{array}{r} 13 \\ -\ 7 \\ \hline 6 \end{array}$$

Think:
1. 13 = 10 + 3
2. Subtract 7 from 10 and then add 3.

Do the subtraction.

③
$$\begin{array}{r} 8 \\ -\ 3 \\ \hline \end{array}$$

④
$$\begin{array}{r} 12 \\ -\ 4 \\ \hline \end{array}$$

⑤
$$\begin{array}{r} 17 \\ -\ 9 \\ \hline \end{array}$$

⑥
$$\begin{array}{r} 6 \\ -\ 1 \\ \hline \end{array}$$

⑦
$$\begin{array}{r} 13 \\ -\ 5 \\ \hline \end{array}$$

⑧
$$\begin{array}{r} 11 \\ -\ 8 \\ \hline \end{array}$$

⑨
$$\begin{array}{r} 9 \\ -\ 2 \\ \hline \end{array}$$

⑩
$$\begin{array}{r} 16 \\ -\ 7 \\ \hline \end{array}$$

⑪ 7 – 4 =

⑫ 11 – 3 =

⑬ 5 – 2 =

⑭ 15 – 8 =

⑮ 10 – 9 =

⑯ 8 – 1 =

⑰ 12 – 6 =

⑱ 10 – 4 =

Canadian Curriculum MathSmart (Grade 2)   ISBN: 978-1-927042-11-3

Find how many cards there are.

⑲

tens	ones
3	2
− 1	8

→

	tens	ones
	(2)	(12)
	3	2
−	1	8

Sometimes when the ones are too small, you need to trade 1 ten for 10 ones to do the subtraction.

⑳
```
   4  5
-  1  2
_____
```

㉑
```
   3  0
-  1  2
_____
```

㉒
```
   7  1
-  2  3
_____
```

㉓
```
   8  1
-  2  0
_____
```

㉔
```
   4  2
-  1  8
_____
```

㉕
```
   9  4
-  6  3
_____
```

㉖ 50 − 48 =

㉗ 55 − 31 =

㉘ 92 − 88 =

㉙ 73 − 37 =

㉚ 71 − 43 =

㉛ 60 − 26 =

㉜ 48 − 19 =

㉝ 83 − 58 =

Vertical Subtraction
Remember to put the numbers in the places: tens to tens and ones to ones

ISBN: 978-1-927042-11-3

Solve the problems.

㉞ There are 41 balloons. If 14 balloons are taken away by the children, how many balloons are left?

☐ balloons are left.

– _____

㉟

– _____

There are 22 red balloons and 15 blue balloons. How many more red balloons are there than blue balloons?

There are ☐ more red balloons than blue balloons.

㊱ a. There are 35 children playing with the clown. If 16 of them are boys, how many girls are there?

☐ – ☐ = ☐

There are ☐ girls.

b. How many more girls are there than boys?

☐ – ☐ = ☐

There are ☐ more girls than boys.

ISBN: 978-1-927042-11-3

See how many points each child gets in the game. Then fill in the blanks.

㊲ _____ gets the most points.

Peter : 46
May : 29
Mike : 37

㊳ Mike gets _____ points more than May.

㊴ May gets _____ points fewer than Peter.

㊵ a. If Jason gets 18 points fewer than Mike, he gets _____ points in the game.

   b. If Elaine gets 25 points more than May, Elaine gets _____ points in the game.

A C T I V I T Y

Read what the frog says. Answer the question.

There are 18 girls and 15 boys playing a game. 24 of them win a prize. What is the smallest number of girls who can win a prize?

_____ girls

ISBN: 978-1-927042-11-3

4 More about Addition and Subtraction

Look at each group of numbers. Complete the number sentences.

> Subtraction is the opposite of addition and vice versa.
> e.g. $12 + 19 = 31$
> $31 - 19 = 12$

① (45) (71) (26)

_____ + _____ = _____

_____ − _____ = _____

② (84) (39) (45)

_____ + _____ = _____

_____ − _____ = _____

③ (16) (52) (36)

_____ + _____ = _____

_____ − _____ = _____

④ (81) (13) (68)

_____ + _____ = _____

_____ − _____ = _____

Write the correct numbers to complete the sentences.

⑤ $9 + 12 = $ _____

_____ $- 12 = 9$

⑥ $18 + 33 = $ _____

_____ $- 33 = 18$

⑦ _____ $- 27 = 15$

$15 + 27 = $ _____

⑧ _____ $- 46 = 26$

$26 + 46 = $ _____

Canadian Curriculum MathSmart (Grade 2)
ISBN: 978-1-927042-11-3

Find the answers.

⑨
```
    6  7
  +    7
  ┌──┬──┐
  │  │  │
  └──┴──┘
```

⑩
```
    4  5
  -    9
  ┌──┬──┐
  │  │  │
  └──┴──┘
```

⑪
```
    3  2
  -  1  4
  ┌──┬──┐
  │  │  │
  └──┴──┘
```

⑫
```
    5  8
  +  3  5
  ┌──┬──┐
  │  │  │
  └──┴──┘
```

⑬
```
    9  0
  -  2  1
  ┌──┬──┐
  │  │  │
  └──┴──┘
```

⑭
```
    3  6
  +  6  3
  ┌──┬──┐
  │  │  │
  └──┴──┘
```

⑮
```
    7  5
  -  3  9
  ┌──┬──┐
  │  │  │
  └──┴──┘
```

⑯
```
    5  0
  -  1  6
  ┌──┬──┐
  │  │  │
  └──┴──┘
```

⑰
```
    4  4
  -  2  6
  ┌──┬──┐
  │  │  │
  └──┴──┘
```

Pay attention to the "+" and "−" signs.

⑱ 28 + 25 =

⑲ 42 − 26 =

⑳ 80 − 55 =

㉑ 68 + 22 =

㉒ 41 − 27 =

㉓ 52 + 19 =

㉔ 16 + 38 =

㉕ 72 − 33 =

ISBN: 978-1-927042-11-3

4

Peter and Jim are at their grandfather's farm. Help them solve the problems.

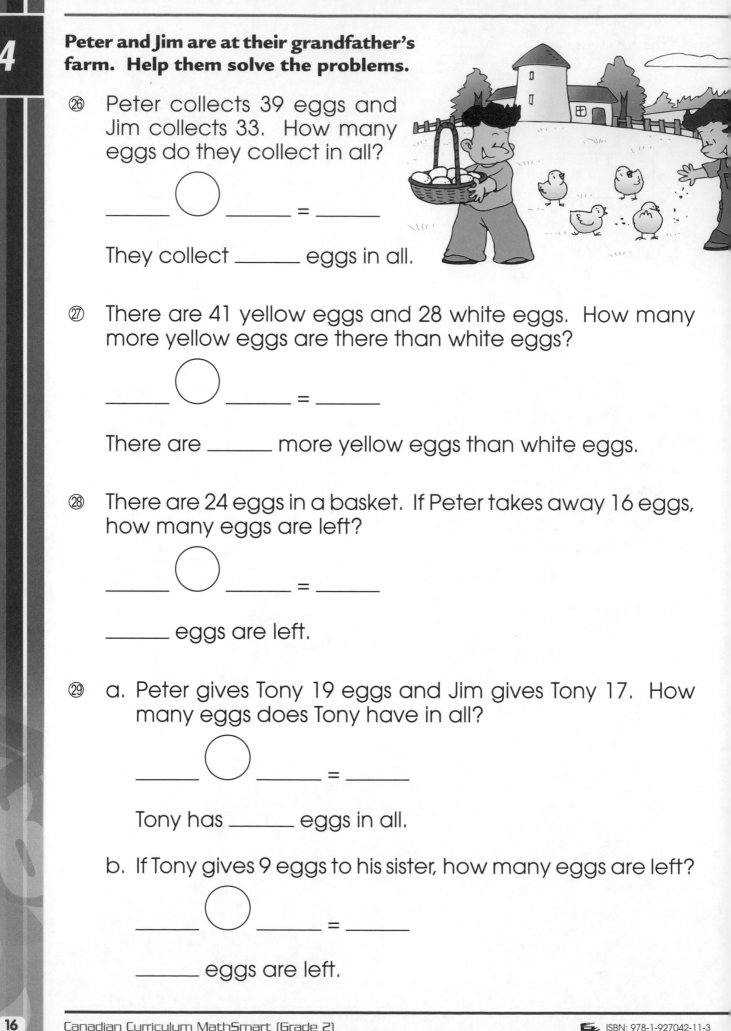

㉖ Peter collects 39 eggs and Jim collects 33. How many eggs do they collect in all?

_____ ◯ _____ = _____

They collect _____ eggs in all.

㉗ There are 41 yellow eggs and 28 white eggs. How many more yellow eggs are there than white eggs?

_____ ◯ _____ = _____

There are _____ more yellow eggs than white eggs.

㉘ There are 24 eggs in a basket. If Peter takes away 16 eggs, how many eggs are left?

_____ ◯ _____ = _____

_____ eggs are left.

㉙ a. Peter gives Tony 19 eggs and Jim gives Tony 17. How many eggs does Tony have in all?

_____ ◯ _____ = _____

Tony has _____ eggs in all.

b. If Tony gives 9 eggs to his sister, how many eggs are left?

_____ ◯ _____ = _____

_____ eggs are left.

Canadian Curriculum MathSmart (Grade 2)   ISBN: 978-1-927042-11-3

Find the answers.

③⓪
```
   3 9
 +   4
 ┌──┬──┐
 │  │  │
 └──┴──┘
 - 2 5
 ┌──┬──┐
 │  │  │
 └──┴──┘
```

③①
```
   6 0
 -   9
 ┌──┬──┐
 │  │  │
 └──┴──┘
 + 1 6
 ┌──┬──┐
 │  │  │
 └──┴──┘
```

③②
```
   2 8
 - 1 3
 ┌──┬──┐
 │  │  │
 └──┴──┘
 +   8
 ┌──┬──┐
 │  │  │
 └──┴──┘
```

③③ 72 − 13 + 25 = _____

③④ 55 + 7 − 44 = _____

③⑤ 30 − 11 + 18 = _____

③⑥ 25 + 26 − 13 = _____

③⑦ 42 − 15 + 9 = _____

Solve the problem from left to right.

e.g.   10 + 11 − 12
       = 9
1st 10 + 11 = 21
2nd 21 − 12 = 9

ACTIVITY

Use a calculator to find the answers. Remember to clear your calculator after each question.

① ☐ 17 ☐ + ☐ 9 ☐ − ☐ 16 ☐ = ☐

② ☐ 28 ☐ − ☐ 13 ☐ + ☐ 4 ☐ = ☐

③ ☐ 35 ☐ + ☐ 23 ☐ + ☐ 16 ☐ − ☐ 13 ☐ = ☐

④ ☐ 46 ☐ + ☐ 29 ☐ − ☐ 17 ☐ − ☐ 4 ☐ = ☐

For question ①, enter:
[1] [7] [+] [9] [−] [1] [6] [=]
Then you'll get the answer.

ISBN: 978-1-927042-11-3

Fill in the missing months and the blanks.

①

January

February

May

July

August

October

December

② There are _____ months in a year.

③ Joe visits the amusement park in _____ . (the 6th month of the year)

④ Vivian will visit the park on July 2. It is a _____ . (a day of the week)

⑤ There are _____ days in July.

⑥ Tim's birthday is on July _____ .

⑦ The month right after July is _____ .

⑧ The day right after July 31 is _____ .

⑨ The day right before July 10 is _____ . It is a _____ .

July 2011

S	M	T	W	T	F	S
					1	2
3	4	5	6	7	8	9
10	11	12	13	14	15	16
17	18	■	20	21	22	23
24	25	26	27	28	29	30
31						

Tim's birthday

There are 7 days in a week.

The first day of the week is Sunday.

ISBN: 978-1-927042-11-3

Read what the mouse says. Then fill in the boxes and write the times in two ways.

When the minute hand goes from one digit to the next, 5 minutes have passed. When the hour hand goes from one digit to the next, 1 hour has passed. On a digital clock, the hour is always shown on the left of ":" , and minutes on the right.

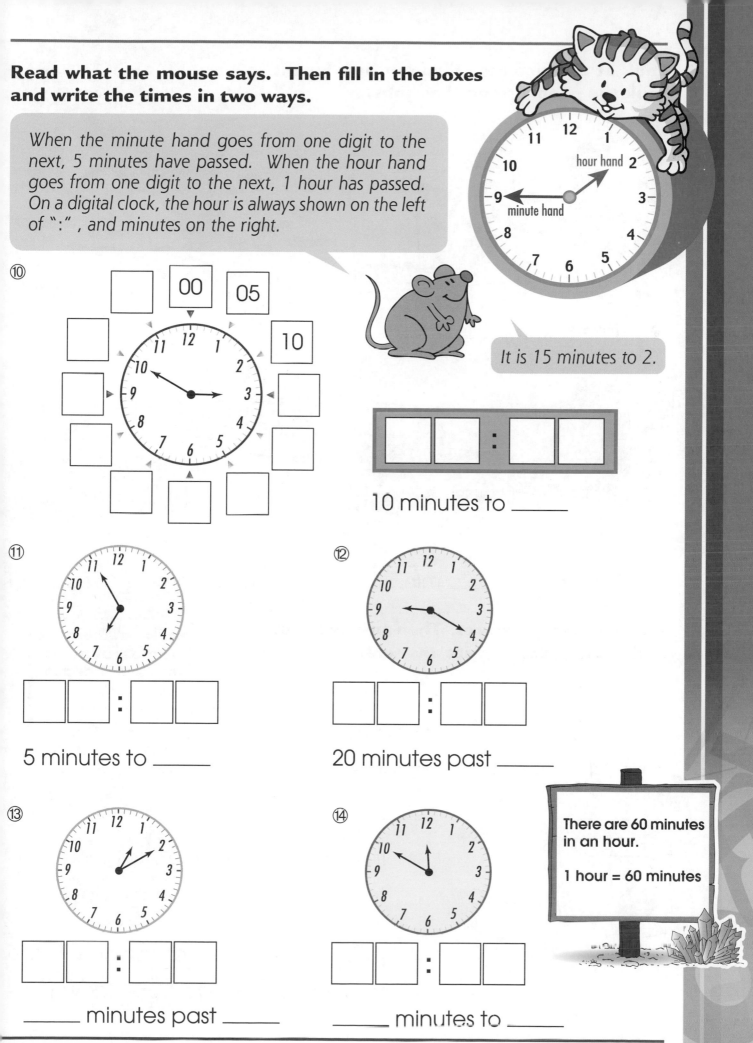

⑩

| 00 | 05 |

| 10 |

It is 15 minutes to 2.

10 minutes to _____

⑪

⬜⬜ : ⬜⬜

5 minutes to _____

⑫

⬜⬜ : ⬜⬜

20 minutes past _____

⑬

⬜⬜ : ⬜⬜

_____ minutes past _____

⑭

⬜⬜ : ⬜⬜

_____ minutes to _____

There are 60 minutes in an hour.

1 hour = 60 minutes

ISBN: 978-1-927042-11-3

Look at the pictures. Find out how long it took the people to do their jobs.

⑮ Time taken: _____ min

⑯ Time taken: _____ min

⑰ Time taken: ___ h ___ min

Write the temperatures. Then answer the question and circle ◯ the correct answers.

⑱

Temperature is measured in degree Celsius (˚C).

e.g. The temperature is 15˚C.

_____ ˚C

_____ ˚C

⑲ Which glass of water is cooler?

_____

⑳ If Jason puts some ice into glass A, the temperature will go   up   down   .

㉑ If Jason heats the water in glass B, the temperature will go   up   down   .

Canadian Curriculum MathSmart (Grade 2)

ISBN: 978-1-927042-11-3

Do the pictures match with the thermometers? Write "likely" or "unlikely" on the lines.

22 _____

23 _____

24 _____

25 _____

Summer is hot and the temperature is high. Winter is cold and the temperature is low.

A C T I V I T Y

Read what Santa Claus says. Fill in the blank.

It is 4:30 now. I'll have a break in 2 hours 15 minutes. What time will it be?

It will be _____ .

ISBN: 978-1-927042-11-3

5

6 Length, Perimeter, and Area

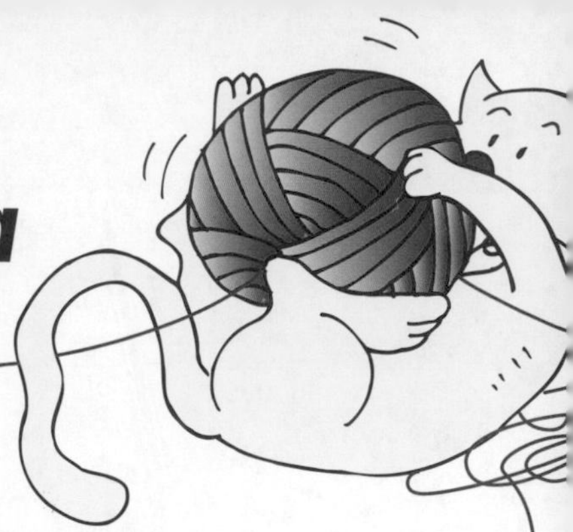

Check ✔ the ones that show the correct way to find the perimeter; otherwise, put a cross ✗.

①

②

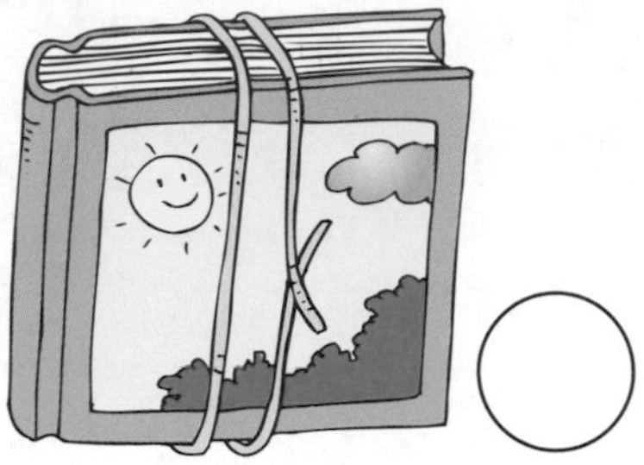

③

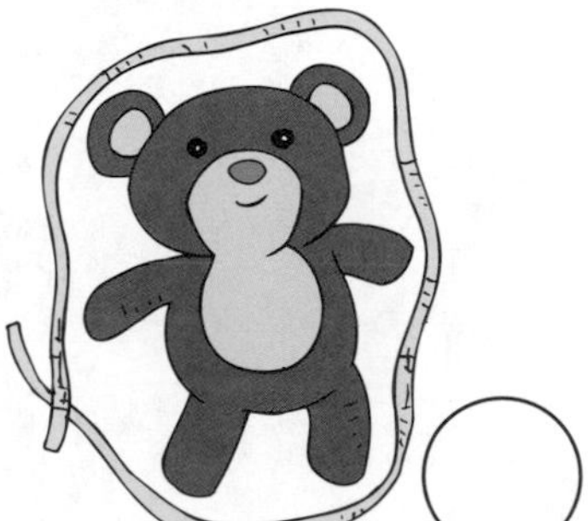

④

CHIPS

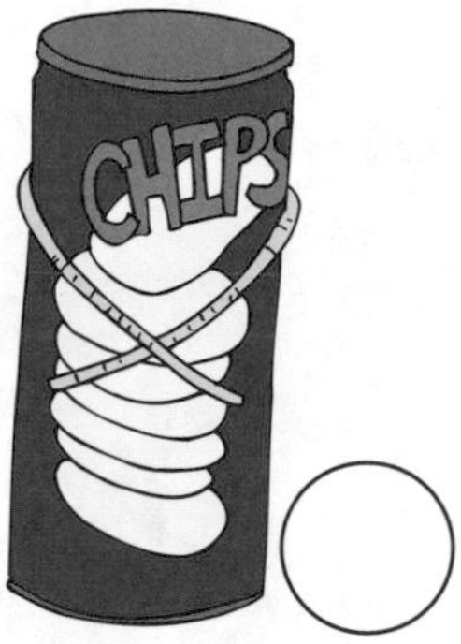

⑤

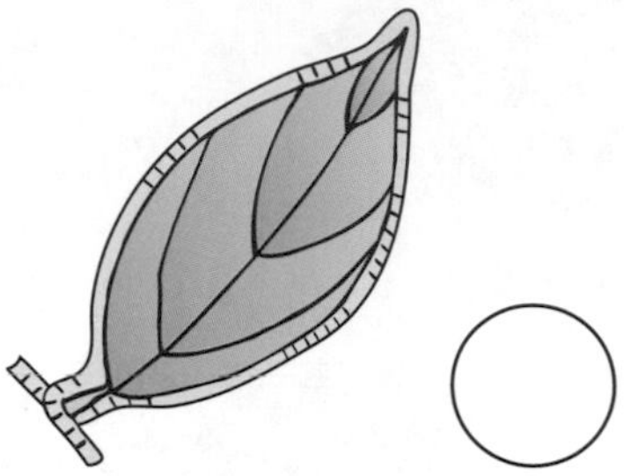

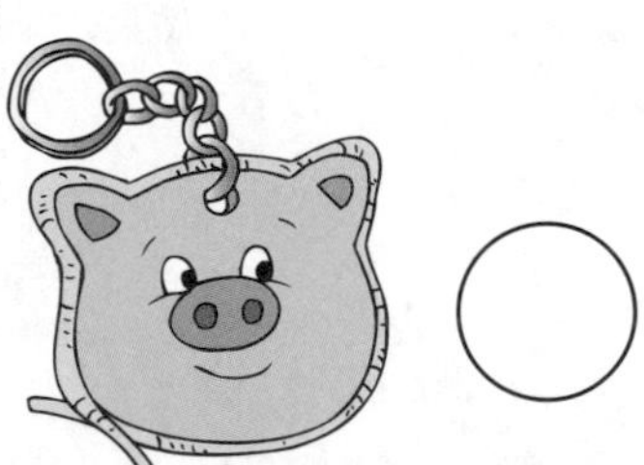

Choose the best unit to do each measurement. Write "m" or "cm".

⑥

cm is short for centimetre.
m is short for metre.

ISBN: 978-1-927042-11-3

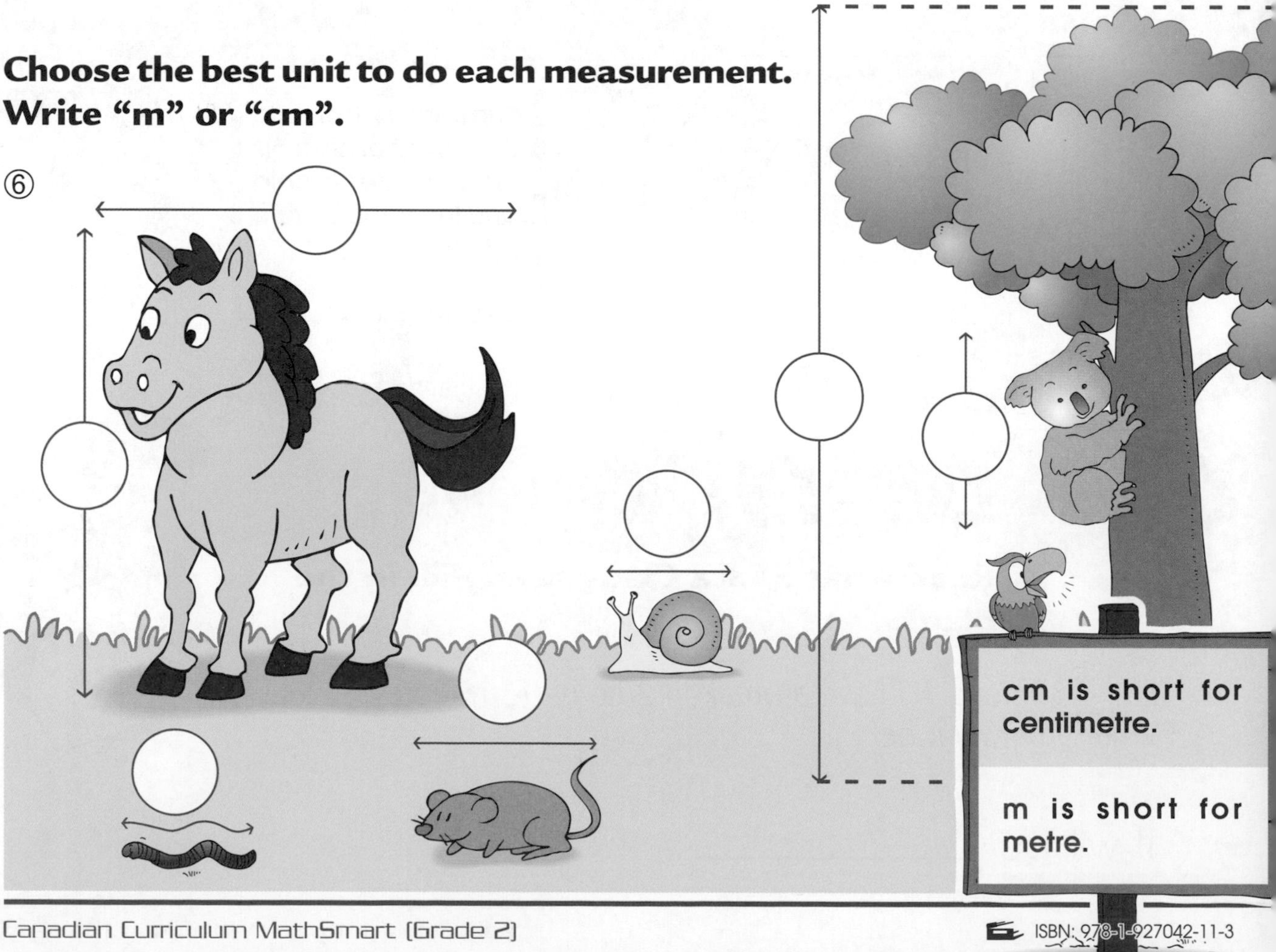

Write the measurements in the boxes.

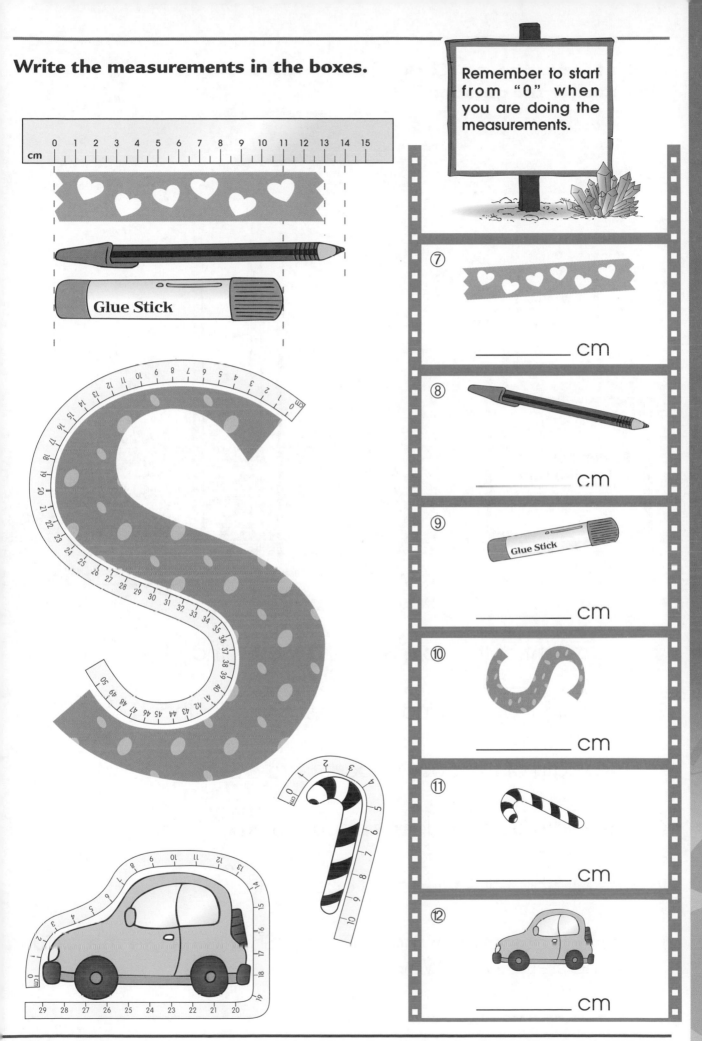

ISBN: 978-1-927042-11-3

Remember to start from "0" when you are doing the measurements.

⑦ _____ cm

⑧ _____ cm

⑨ _____ cm

⑩ _____ cm

⑪ _____ cm

⑫ _____ cm

Glue Stick

6

**Look at Steve's house. Circle ◯ the correct answers.
Then answer the question.**

Remember:
1 m = 100 cm

⑬ The height of the door is [less   more] than 1 m.

⑭ The height of the window is [less   more] than 1 m.

⑮ The width of the door is about [1 m   3 m] .

⑯ The width of the ladder is about [5 cm   25 cm] .

⑰ The width of the window is about [1 m   4 m] .

⑱ Steve is going to fix the chimney. Should he use the ladder
or the step stool? Why?

_____

ISBN: 978-1-927042-11-3

Find the number of tiles needed to cover the rooftop of each building. Then answer the question.

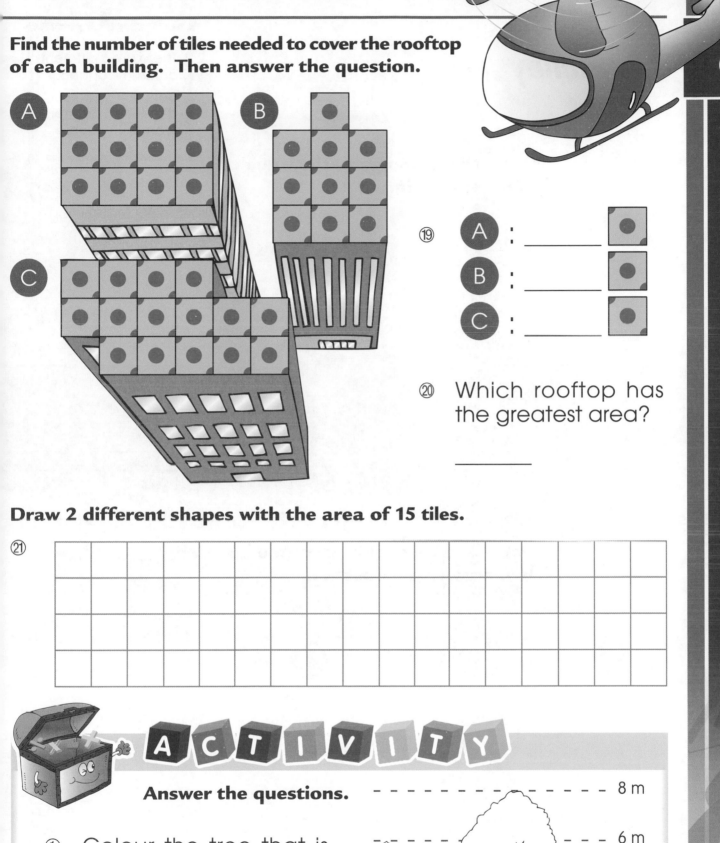

A

B

C

⑲

A : _____

B : _____

C : _____

⑳ Which rooftop has the greatest area?

_____

Draw 2 different shapes with the area of 15 tiles.

㉑

ACTIVITY

Answer the questions.

① Colour the tree that is about 5 m tall.

② There is/are _____ tree(s) shorter than 7 m.

8 m

6 m

4 m

2 m

7 Money

There are 6 different coins in Canada:

penny   nickel
dime   quarter
loonie   toonie

Name and write the value of each coin.

① _____ ;

_____

② _____ ;

_____

③ _____ ;

④ _____ ; _____

⑤ _____ ;

⑥ _____ ;

Find the value of the coins in each group.
Then answer the question.

⑦

A _____

B _____

C _____

⑧ Which group shows the value of $1?   ◯

Canadian Curriculum MathSmart (Grade 2)   ISBN: 978-1-927042-11-3

Write the price of each toy on its price tag.
Then answer the questions.

⑨

⑩ Which toy costs the most?

_____

⑪ Peter has 65¢. Which toy can he buy?

_____

⑫ Mabel is buying an elephant. If she buys a bear instead, how much more does she need to pay?

_____ ¢

⑬ Stephanie buys a giraffe with a coupon of 16¢ . How much does she need to pay?

_____ ¢

ISBN: 978-1-927042-11-3

7

Check ✔ the correct coins or write the fewest coins to match how much each child has.

⑭ 4 coins are worth 41¢.

⑮ 5 coins are worth 42¢.

⑯ I have 82¢ in all.

⑰ I have 69¢ in all.

ISBN: 978-1-927042-11-3

Answer the questions.

⑱ Tony has 60¢. If he buys a [Puzzle], how much will he have left?

☐ − ☐ = ☐

He will have ☐ ¢ left.

⑲ Rhoda has 91¢. If she buys a 🚗, she will have 16¢ left. How much does the car cost?

☐ − ☐ = ☐   It costs ☐ ¢.

⑳ Lily has 59¢. How much more does she need to pay for a bear?

☐ − ☐ = ☐   She needs to pay ☐ ¢ more.

ACTIVITY

Check ✔ the 3 things that cost exactly 90¢ in all.

A 34¢

B pop 75¢

C 17¢

D 18¢

E Juice 55¢

F 25¢

ISBN: 978-1-927042-11-3

Canadian Curriculum MathSmart (Grade 2)

8 Shapes

Annie used wires to make a sculpture. Name the shapes.

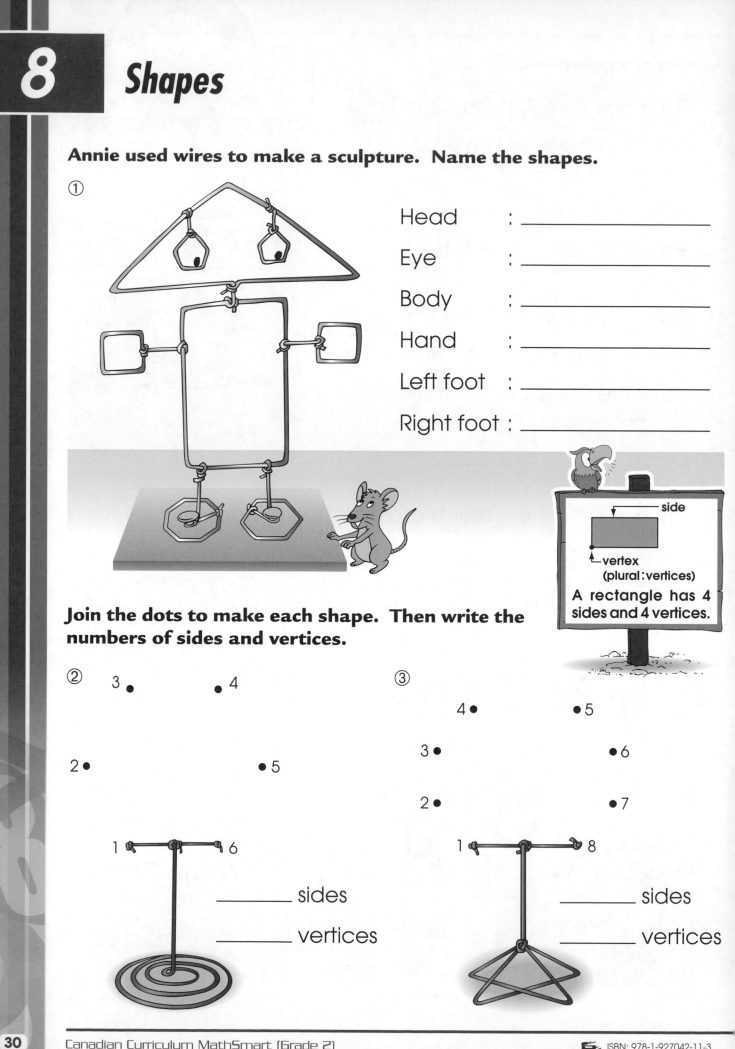

①

Head : _____

Eye : _____

Body : _____

Hand : _____

Left foot : _____

Right foot : _____

side

vertex
(plural : vertices)

A rectangle has 4 sides and 4 vertices.

Join the dots to make each shape. Then write the numbers of sides and vertices.

② 3● ●4

2● ●5

1 6

_____ sides

_____ vertices

③ 4● ●5

3● ●6

2● ●7

1 8

_____ sides

_____ vertices

ISBN: 978-1-927042-11-3

Fill in the blanks.

④ A triangle has _____ sides and _____ vertices.

⑤ A square has _____ sides and _____ vertices.

⑥ A/An _____ has 5 sides and 5 vertices.

⑦ A/An _____ has 8 sides and 8 vertices.

Look at the patterns. Write the names of the two different shapes in each pattern.

⑧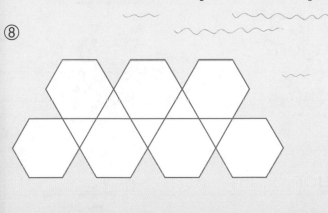

⑨

_____ ; _____   _____ ; _____

⑩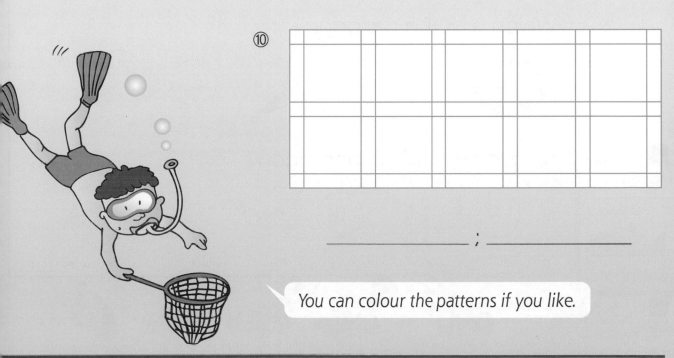

_____ ; _____

You can colour the patterns if you like.

ISBN: 978-1-927042-11-3

8

Check ✔ the correct answers.

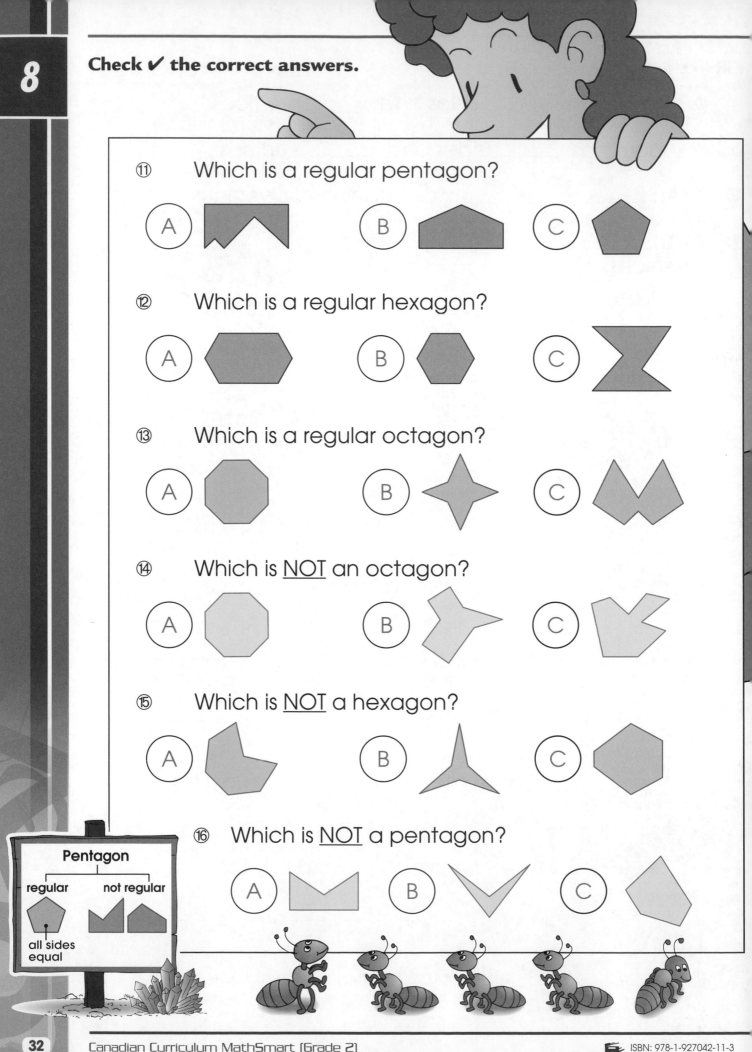

⑪ Which is a regular pentagon?

Ⓐ   Ⓑ   Ⓒ

⑫ Which is a regular hexagon?

Ⓐ   Ⓑ   Ⓒ

⑬ Which is a regular octagon?

Ⓐ   Ⓑ   Ⓒ

⑭ Which is <u>NOT</u> an octagon?

Ⓐ   Ⓑ   Ⓒ

⑮ Which is <u>NOT</u> a hexagon?

Ⓐ   Ⓑ   Ⓒ

⑯ Which is <u>NOT</u> a pentagon?

Ⓐ   Ⓑ   Ⓒ

Pentagon

regular   not regular

all sides equal

The dotted line is the line of symmetry of each shape. Draw the other half of the shape.

You can also put a mirror on the line of symmetry to see how the other half looks.

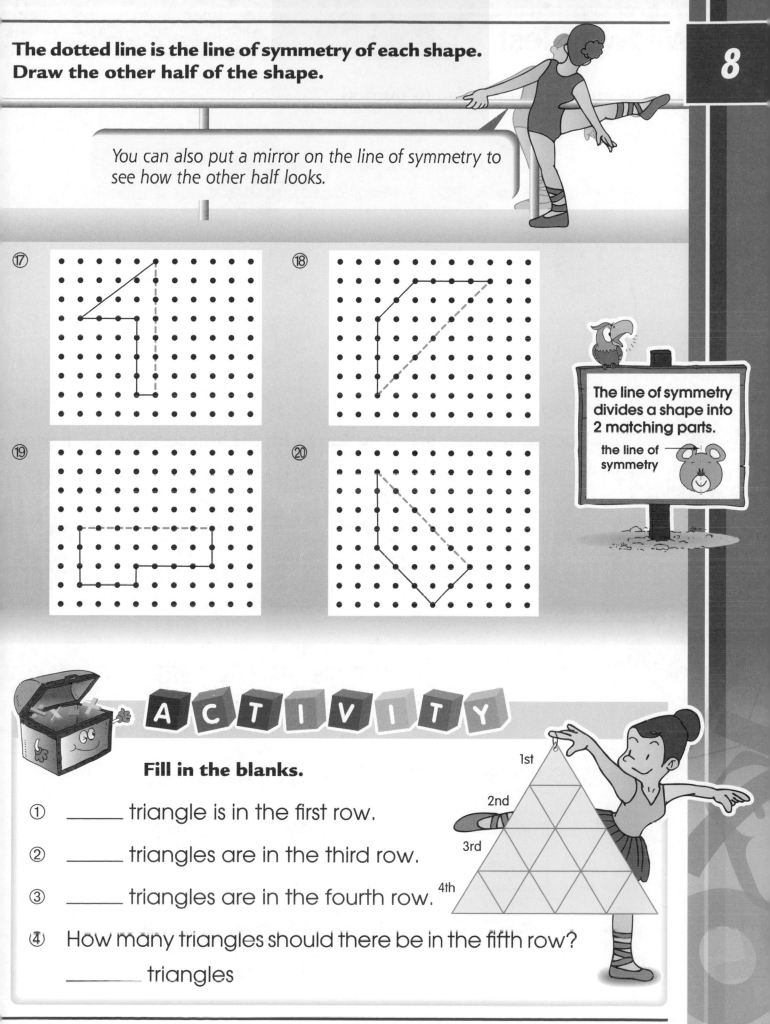

The line of symmetry divides a shape into 2 matching parts.

the line of symmetry

ACTIVITY

Fill in the blanks.

① _____ triangle is in the first row.

② _____ triangles are in the third row.

③ _____ triangles are in the fourth row.

④ How many triangles should there be in the fifth row?

_____ triangles

1st
2nd
3rd
4th

ISBN: 978-1-927042-11-3

Midway Test

Write the numbers in words. (6 marks)

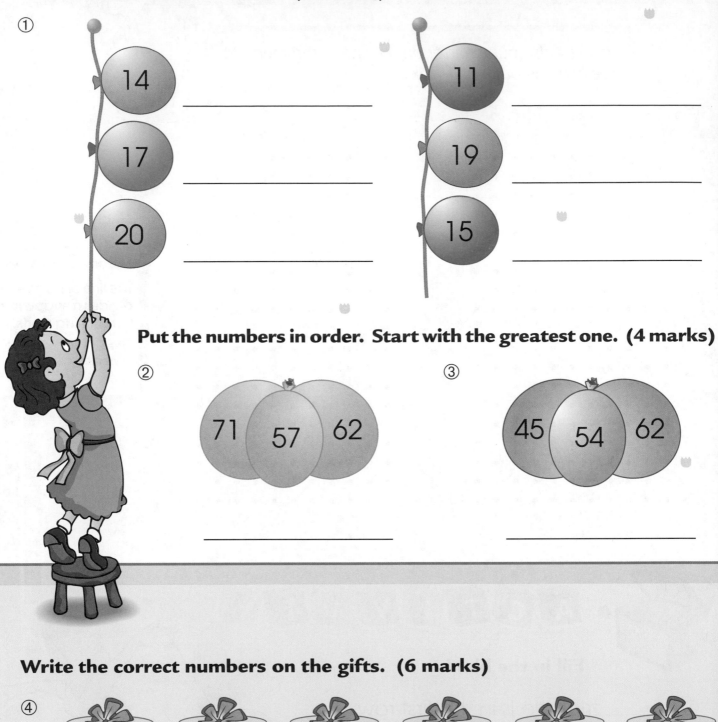

① 14 _____

17 _____

20 _____

11 _____

19 _____

15 _____

Put the numbers in order. Start with the greatest one. (4 marks)

② 71 57 62

_____

③ 45 54 62

_____

Write the correct numbers on the gifts. (6 marks)

④ 77 78 ___ ___ 81 ___

⑤ 92 90 ___ ___ 86 ___

ISBN: 978-1-927042-11-3

Count and write the numbers. (4 marks)

⑥

⑦

Find the answers. (20 marks)

⑧
```
  3 7
+ 2 5
```

⑨
```
  4 6
- 2 9
```

⑩
```
  8 0
- 1 8
```

⑪
```
  1 2
+ 6 8
```

⑫
```
  8 5
- 3 4
```

⑬
```
  6 6
+ 2 7
```

⑭ 71 − 42 =

⑮ 55 + 15 =

⑯ 38 + 18 =

⑰ 63 − 36 =

Look at the shapes. Then write their names and answer the questions. (11 marks)

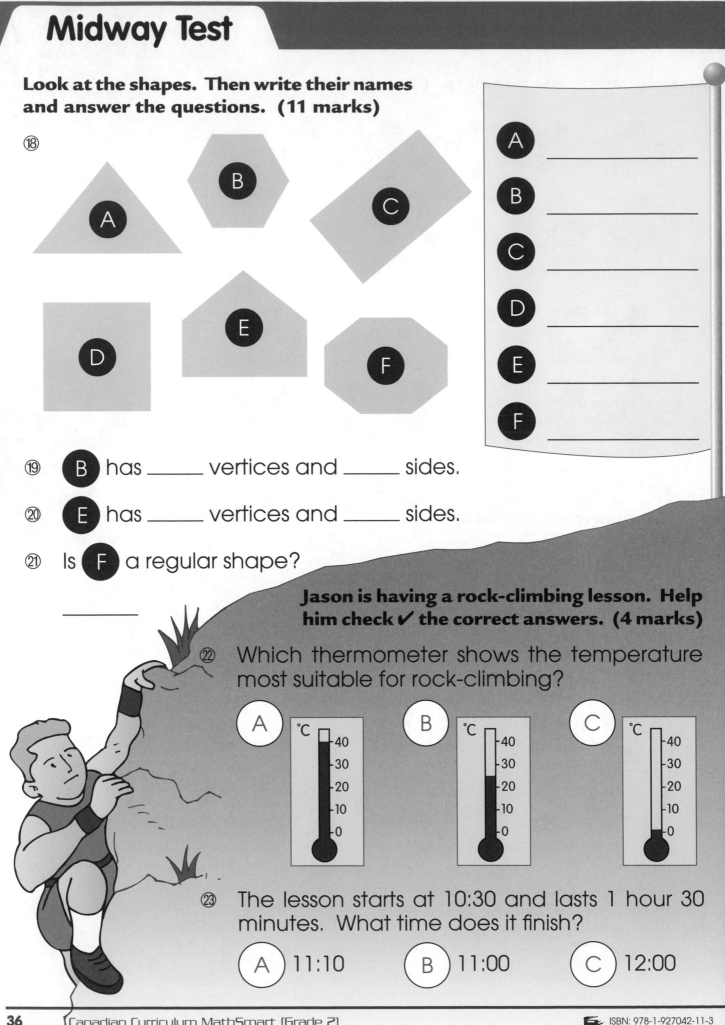

⑱

A _____

B _____

C _____

D _____

E _____

F _____

⑲ B has _____ vertices and _____ sides.

⑳ E has _____ vertices and _____ sides.

㉑ Is F a regular shape?

_____

Jason is having a rock-climbing lesson. Help him check ✔ the correct answers. (4 marks)

㉒ Which thermometer shows the temperature most suitable for rock-climbing?

A °C 40 30 20 10 0

B °C 40 30 20 10 0

C °C 40 30 20 10 0

㉓ The lesson starts at 10:30 and lasts 1 hour 30 minutes. What time does it finish?

A) 11:10   B) 11:00   C) 12:00

ISBN: 978-1-927042-11-3

Look at the hill that Jason is going to climb. Help him solve the problems. (5 marks)

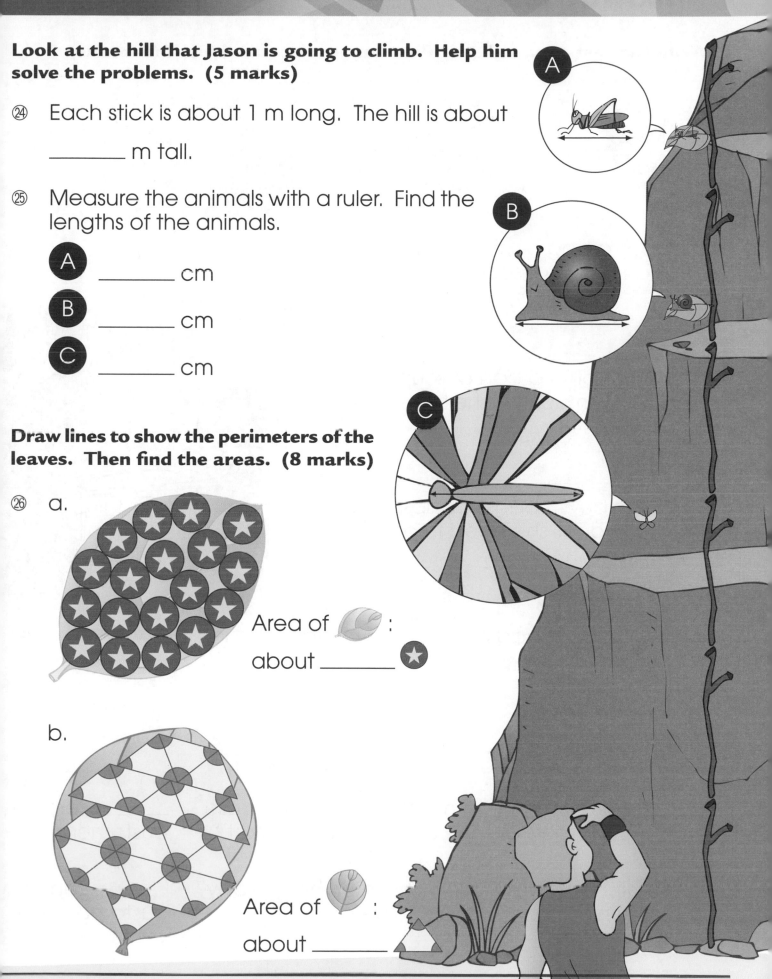

㉔ Each stick is about 1 m long. The hill is about

_____ m tall.

㉕ Measure the animals with a ruler. Find the lengths of the animals.

Ⓐ _____ cm

Ⓑ _____ cm

Ⓒ _____ cm

Draw lines to show the perimeters of the leaves. Then find the areas. (8 marks)

㉖ a.

Area of 🐚 :

about _____ ⭐

b.

Area of 🍃 :

about _____

ISBN: 978-1-927042-11-3

Write the cost of each item. Then answer the questions. (16 marks)

㉗

㉘ Does a bag of chips cost more than a can of soup?

_____

㉙ If Doris buys a can of soup with $1, how much will she have left?

_____ ¢

㉚ If Ann buys 2 bags of chips, how much does she need to pay?

_____ ¢

㉛ If Tim buys 1 bag of chips, he will have 26¢ left. How much does he have?

_____ ¢

㉜ There are 96 customers in the supermarket.

a. If 38 of them are male, how many female customers are there in the supermarket?

_____ female customers

b. If 19 of them are not senior, how many senior customers are there?

_____ senior customers

ISBN: 978-1-927042-11-3

Circle ◯ the correct signs. Then solve the problems. (8 marks)

㉝ Janet has 37 bottles of bubble soap and Mark has 28. How many bottles of bubble soap do they have in all?

_____ **+** **–** _____ = _____

_____ bottles

㉞ Sue and Dan have 61 bottles of bubble soap in all. If Sue has 29 bottles, how many bottles of bubble soap does Dan have?

_____ **+** **–** _____ = _____

_____ bottles

Find the answers. (8 marks)

㉟ If a bottle of bubble soap costs 29¢, how much do two bottles of bubble soap cost?

_____ = _____

They cost _____ ¢.

㊱ If Jason pays for a bottle of bubble soap with 2 quarters, what will be his change?

_____ = _____

His change will be _____ ¢.

Score

100

9 Multiplication and Division

Ron and his family had a barbecue yesterday. Count and write the amount of food they ate.

① 3 groups of 6

= _____ + _____ + _____

= _____ sixes

= _____

Multiplication is repeated addition.
e.g.   2 groups of 3
= 3 + 3
= 2 threes
= 6

② 2 groups of 4

= _____ + _____

= _____ fours

= _____

③ 4 groups of 10

= _____ + _____ + _____ + _____

= _____ tens

= _____

④ 5 groups of 5

= _____ + _____ + _____ + _____ + _____

= _____ fives

= _____

ISBN: 978-1-927042-11-3

Find the number of insects.

⑤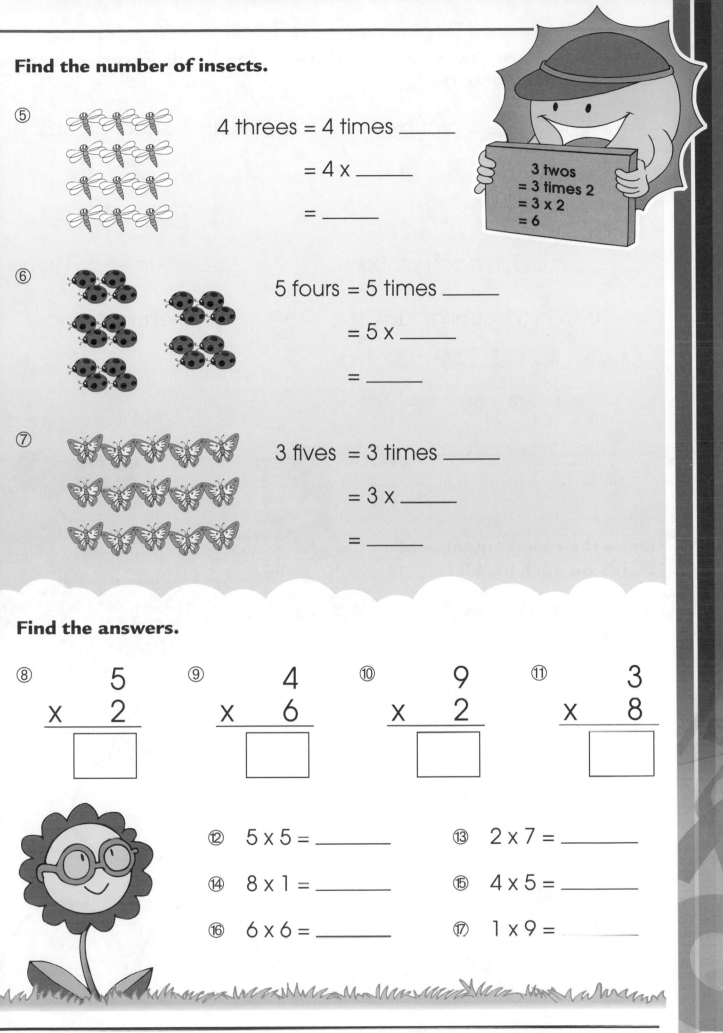

4 threes = 4 times _____

= 4 x _____

= _____

3 twos
= 3 times 2
= 3 x 2
= 6

⑥

5 fours = 5 times _____

= 5 x _____

= _____

⑦

3 fives = 3 times _____

= 3 x _____

= _____

Find the answers.

⑧
```
    5
x   2
```

⑨
```
    4
x   6
```

⑩
```
    9
x   2
```

⑪
```
    3
x   8
```

⑫ 5 x 5 = _____

⑬ 2 x 7 = _____

⑭ 8 x 1 = _____

⑮ 4 x 5 = _____

⑯ 6 x 6 = _____

⑰ 1 x 9 = _____

The children are sharing beads. Circle ◯ the beads in correct groups and write the numbers.

⑱ 9 🫙 in 3 equal groups

_____ 🫙 in each group

⑲ 8 🔵 in 4 equal groups

_____ 🔵 in each group

⑳ 10 ❤️ in 5 equal groups

_____ ❤️ in each group

㉑ 6 ⭐ in 2 equal groups

_____ ⭐ in each group

Draw the correct number of beads on each necklace.

There are the same number of beads on each necklace.

㉒ 24 🫙 for 4 necklaces

㉓ 15 ❤️ for 3 necklaces

Canadian Curriculum MathSmart (Grade 2)   ISBN: 978-1-927042-11-3

Solve the problems.

㉔ There are 8 ◇ in a bracelet. How many ◇ are there in 3 bracelets?

_____

㉕ A bag can hold 5 ◇. A box can hold 4 times as many ◇ as a bag. How many ◇ can be held in a box?

_____

㉖ 6 🏴‍☠️ are sharing 12 ◇. How many ◇ does each 🏴‍☠️ get?

_____

㉗ There are 36 🏆 in a box. If each 🏴‍☠️ can have 9 🏆, how many 🏴‍☠️ are there?

_____

ACTIVITY

Do the questions and colour the correct answers to find the way to the treasure.

① 4 x 3	
② 6 x 5	30 20 2 32 20 0
③ 10 x 2	
④ 8 x 9	
⑤ 7 x 5	Enter 12 72 35 0 36 25
⑥ 4 x 1	
⑦ 6 x 4	
⑧ 10 x 0	
⑨ 9 x 4	14 36 4 24 10 32
⑩ 5 x 5	

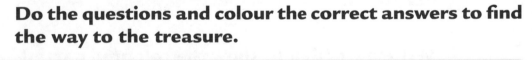

10 Fractions

one half $= \frac{1}{2}$

one third $= \frac{1}{3}$

one fourth $= \frac{1}{4}$
(one quarter)

Colour the pizzas.

① Colour one half of each pizza.

② Colour two thirds of each pizza.

③ Colour three quarters of each pizza.

Write a fraction to show the coloured part of each figure.

④ ⑤ ⑥

_____   _____   _____

A fraction shows a part of a whole.
e.g.

↳ 1 part coloured

$\frac{1}{4}$ is coloured.

↳ 4 equal parts

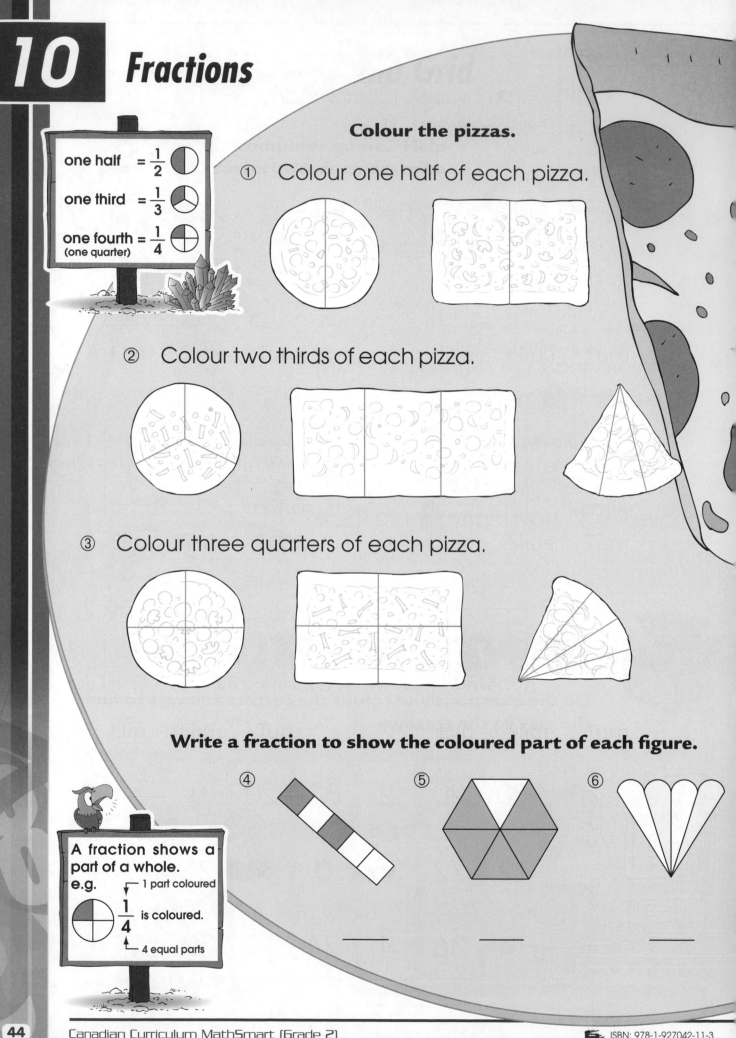

Canadian Curriculum MathSmart (Grade 2)
ISBN: 978-1-927042-11-3

Take a look at the pizzas. Write numbers or fractions to complete the sentences.

⑦ a. _____ out of _____ pizzas are pepperoni.

b. _____ of the pizzas are pepperoni.

Hawaiian
Pepperoni

Hawaiian
Hawaiian
Pepperoni
Pepperoni
Pepperoni
Hawaiian

Pepperoni
Pepperoni
Hawaiian
Hawaiian
Pepperoni

⑧ a. _____ out of _____ pizzas are Hawaiian.

b. _____ of the pizzas are Hawaiian.

▲ ▲ ▲ ★ ★

(3 triangles and 2 stars)
2 out of 5 shapes are stars.
$\frac{2}{5}$ of the shapes are stars.

Colour the shapes to show the fractions. Then circle ◯ the correct words.

⑨ $\frac{1}{3}$ $\frac{1}{5}$ $\frac{1}{3}$ is   greater   smaller   than $\frac{1}{5}$.

⑩ $\frac{4}{9}$ $\frac{5}{6}$ $\frac{4}{9}$ is   greater   smaller   than $\frac{5}{6}$.

ACTIVITY

Colour the pizza.

Peter cuts the pizza into 8 equal slices. If he takes $\frac{1}{2}$ of the pizza, how many slices are left? Colour them.

11 Solids

Colour the prisms yellow and the pyramids green.

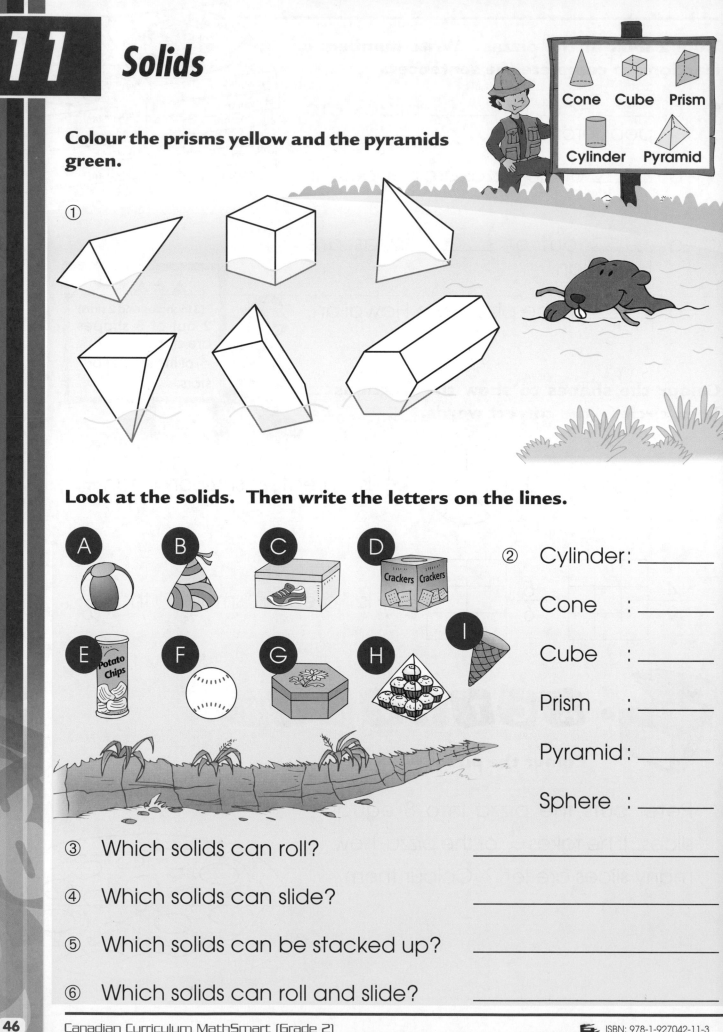

Cone Cube Prism
Cylinder Pyramid

①

Look at the solids. Then write the letters on the lines.

A B C D
Crackers Crackers

E F G H I
Potato Chips

② Cylinder: _____

Cone : _____

Cube : _____

Prism : _____

Pyramid : _____

Sphere : _____

③ Which solids can roll? _____

④ Which solids can slide? _____

⑤ Which solids can be stacked up? _____

⑥ Which solids can roll and slide? _____

ISBN: 978-1-927042-11-3

Join the dots. Name the solids. Then solve the problems.

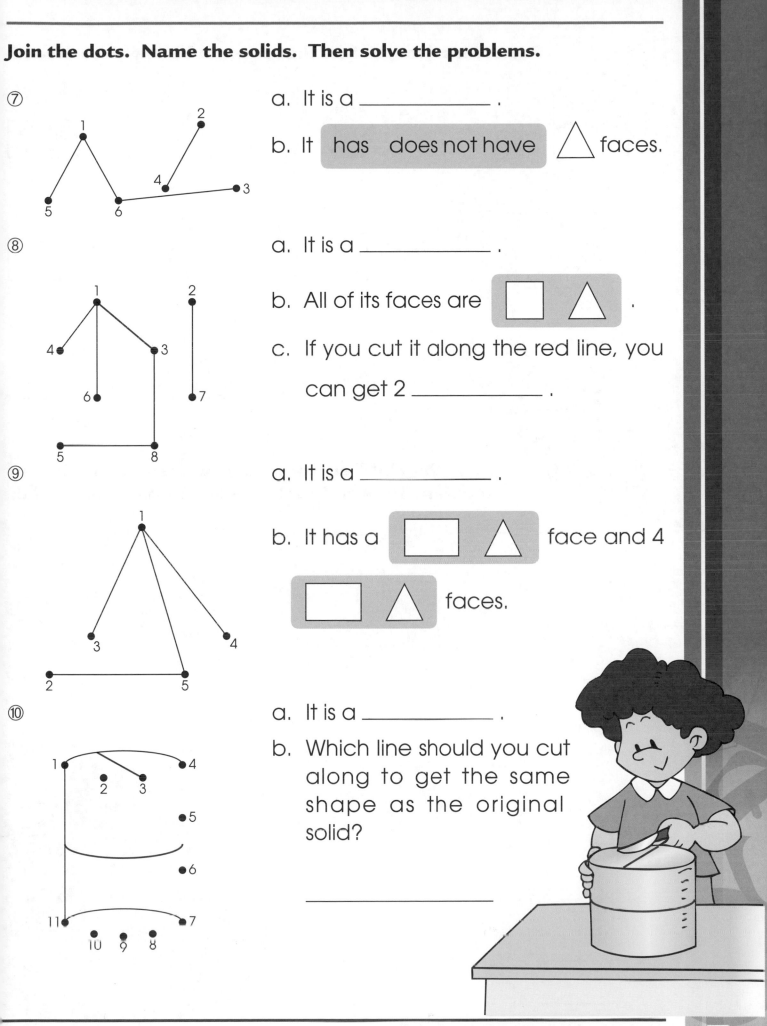

⑦

a. It is a _____ .

b. It ⟨ has   does not have ⟩ △ faces.

⑧

a. It is a _____ .

b. All of its faces are ⟨ □ △ ⟩ .

c. If you cut it along the red line, you can get 2 _____ .

⑨

a. It is a _____ .

b. It has a ⟨ □ △ ⟩ face and 4 ⟨ □ △ ⟩ faces.

⑩

a. It is a _____ .

b. Which line should you cut along to get the same shape as the original solid?

_____

ISBN: 978-1-927042-11-3

11

Put a cross ✗ for the face that does not belong to each solid.

⑪

Ⓐ ⬡ Ⓑ ▲ Ⓒ ▭

⑫

Ⓐ △ Ⓑ ⬟ Ⓒ ▭

⑬

Ⓐ ◼ Ⓑ ▬ Ⓒ ▲

Help the children count and write the number of marshmallows and sticks needed to build each solid.

⑭

⑮

⑯

⑰

⑱

Canadian Curriculum MathSmart (Grade 2)   ISBN: 978-1-927042-11-3

Write the names of the two solids in each model.

⑲

A _____ , _____

B _____ , _____

C _____ , _____

D _____ , _____

E _____ , _____

F _____ , _____

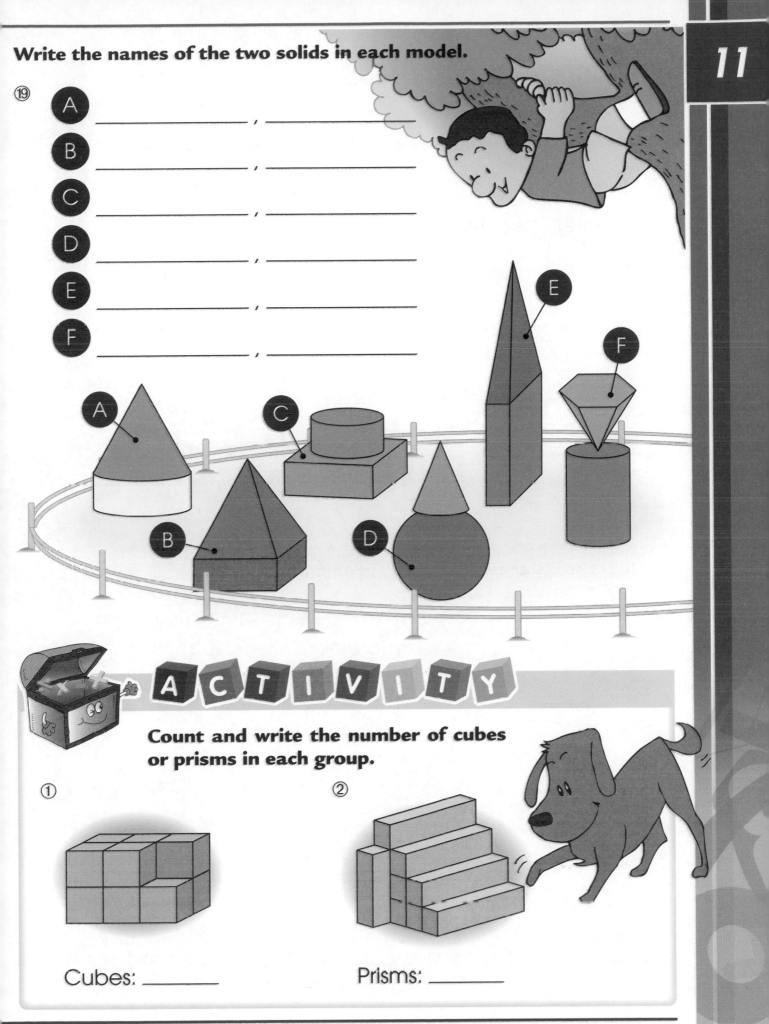

Count and write the number of cubes or prisms in each group.

①

②

Cubes: _____

Prisms: _____

12

Capacity and Mass

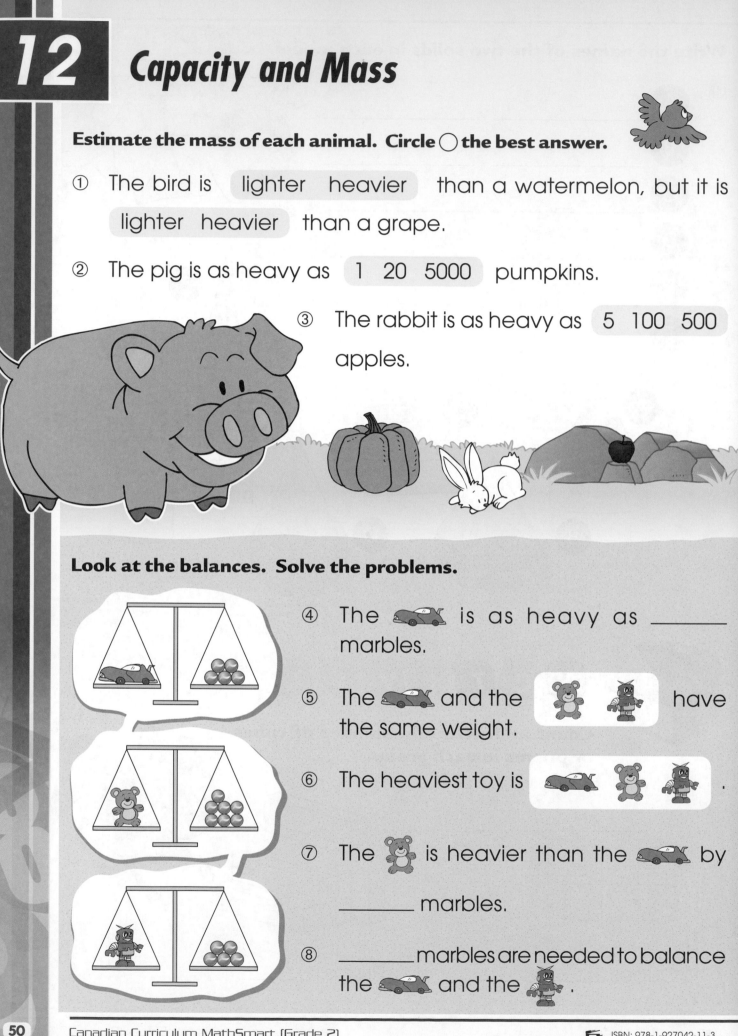

Estimate the mass of each animal. Circle ◯ the best answer.

① The bird is ⟨ lighter   heavier ⟩ than a watermelon, but it is ⟨ lighter   heavier ⟩ than a grape.

② The pig is as heavy as ⟨ 1   20   5000 ⟩ pumpkins.

③ The rabbit is as heavy as ⟨ 5   100   500 ⟩ apples.

Look at the balances. Solve the problems.

④ The 🚗 is as heavy as _____ marbles.

⑤ The 🚗 and the 🧸🤖 have the same weight.

⑥ The heaviest toy is 🚗 🧸 🤖 .

⑦ The 🧸 is heavier than the 🚗 by _____ marbles.

⑧ _____ marbles are needed to balance the 🚗 and the 🤖 .

Canadian Curriculum MathSmart (Grade 2)   ISBN: 978-1-927042-11-3

Find out how many glasses of water each container can hold. Then answer the questions.

The more glasses of water the container can hold, the greater its capacity is.

⑨  =

_____ glasses of water

⑩ _____ glasses of water

⑪ _____ glasses of water

⑫ _____ holds 7 more glasses of water than _____ .

⑬ _____ of water are needed to fill up a _____ .

⑭ Put the containers in order from the one with the greatest capacity. Write the numbers 1 – 3.

ACTIVITY

How many of water are needed to fill up a ?

= 10   = 2   _____

13 Graphs

Look at the graph and answer the questions.

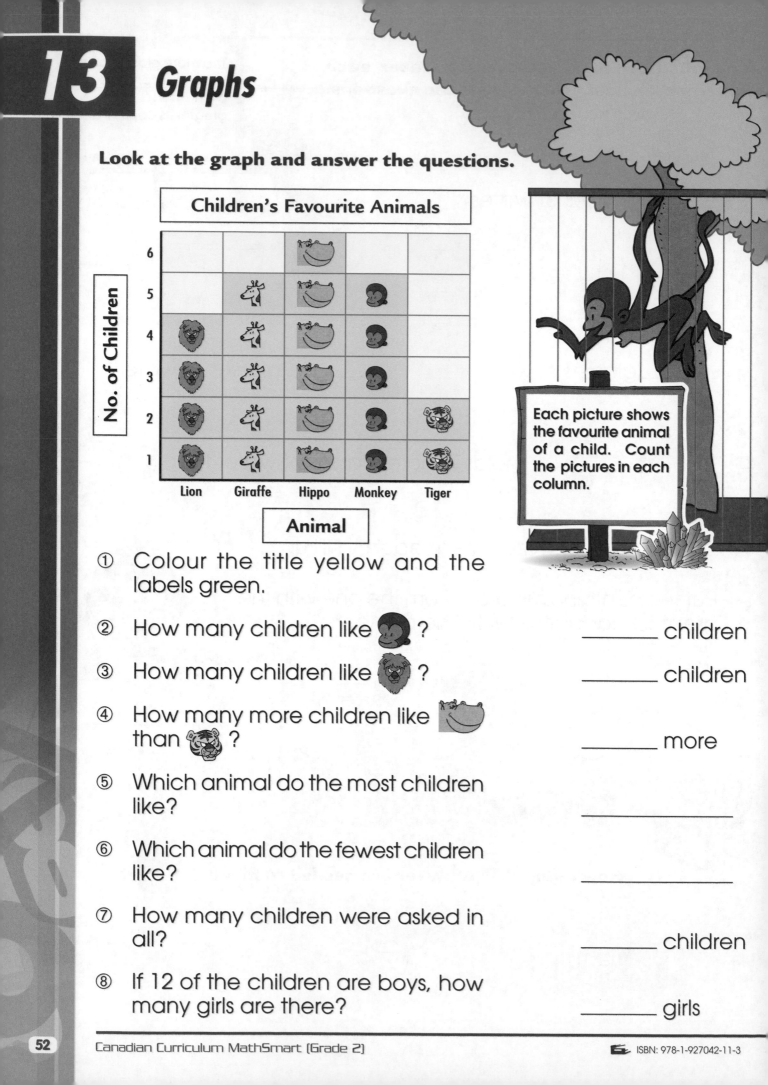

Each picture shows the favourite animal of a child. Count the pictures in each column.

① Colour the title yellow and the labels green.

② How many children like 🐒 ?   _____ children

③ How many children like 🦁 ?   _____ children

④ How many more children like 🦛 than 🐯 ?   _____ more

⑤ Which animal do the most children like?   _____

⑥ Which animal do the fewest children like?   _____

⑦ How many children were asked in all?   _____ children

⑧ If 12 of the children are boys, how many girls are there?   _____ girls

ISBN: 978-1-927042-11-3

Read the graph and answer the questions.

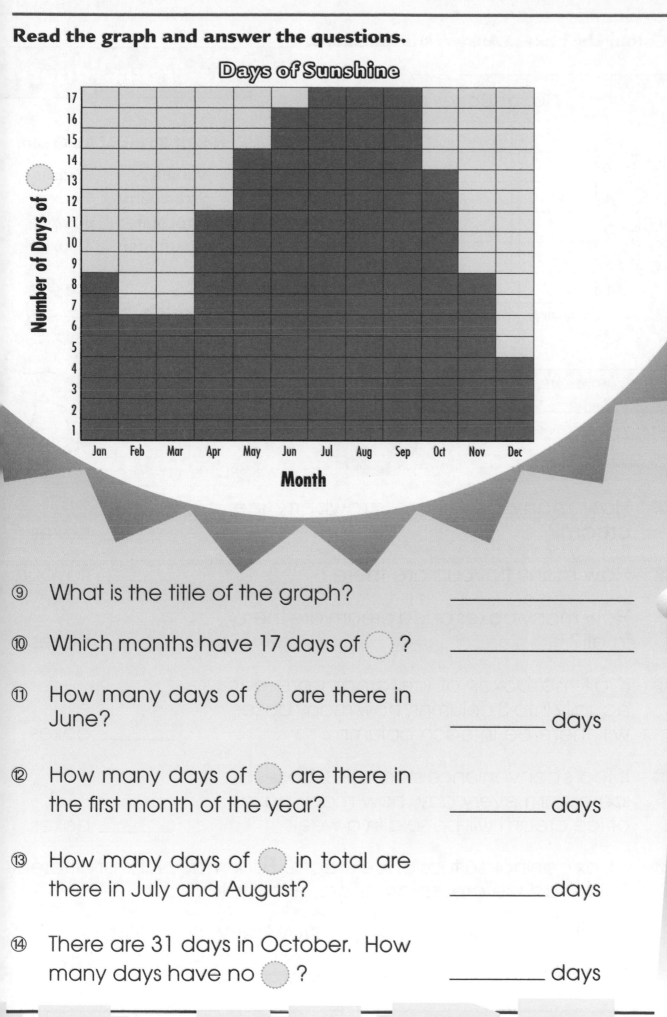

Days of Sunshine

Number of Days of ◯

Jan Feb Mar Apr May Jun Jul Aug Sep Oct Nov Dec

Month

⑨ What is the title of the graph? _____

⑩ Which months have 17 days of ◯ ? _____

⑪ How many days of ◯ are there in June? _____ days

⑫ How many days of ◯ are there in the first month of the year? _____ days

⑬ How many days of ◯ in total are there in July and August? _____ days

⑭ There are 31 days in October. How many days have no ◯ ? _____ days

13

Colour the boxes. Answer the questions.

Ice Cream Factory

⑮ **No. of Boxes of Ice Cream**

Number of Boxes

6
5
4
3
2
1

Vanilla   Strawberry   Chocolate   Neapolitan

Ice Cream

No. of Boxes of Ice Cream

Vanilla	3 boxes
Strawberry	5 boxes
Chocolate	6 boxes
Neapolitan	4 boxes

ICE CREAM

Vanilla

⑯ How many boxes are strawberry ice cream? _____ boxes

⑰ How many flavours are there? _____ flavours

⑱ How many boxes of ice cream are there in all? _____ boxes

⑲ If all the boxes of ice cream are put equally into 3 columns, how many boxes will there be in each column? _____ boxes

⑳ If Ted's convenience store sells 2 boxes of ice cream every day, how many boxes of ice cream will be sold in a week? _____ boxes

㉑ 1 box can hold 6 tubs of ice cream. How many tubs of different flavoured ice cream are there in the truck?

Vanilla : _____ tubs   Strawberry : _____ tubs

Chocolate : _____ tubs   Neapolitan : _____ tubs

Colour and complete the graph. Then answer the questions.

㉒ **Number of Fish Caught**

	Sunfish	Catfish	Perch	Bass
8				
7				
6				
5				
4				
3				
2				
1				

Number of Fish Caught

Sunfish   3
Catfish   8
Perch   4
Bass   2

㉓ Uncle Philip catches _____ fewer sunfish than catfish.

㉔ _____ fish are caught in all.

㉕ If Uncle Philip releases all the perch into the lake, he will have _____ fish left.

㉖ One dozen worms costs 3 dollars. If Uncle Philip buys 3 dozen worms , he needs to pay _____ dollars.

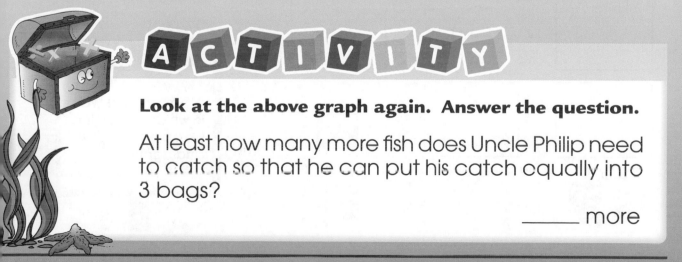

ACTIVITY

Look at the above graph again. Answer the question.

At least how many more fish does Uncle Philip need to catch so that he can put his catch equally into 3 bags?

_____ more

ISBN: 978-1-927042-11-3

14 Patterning

Follow the patterns. Draw the missing pictures.

Complete the patterns.

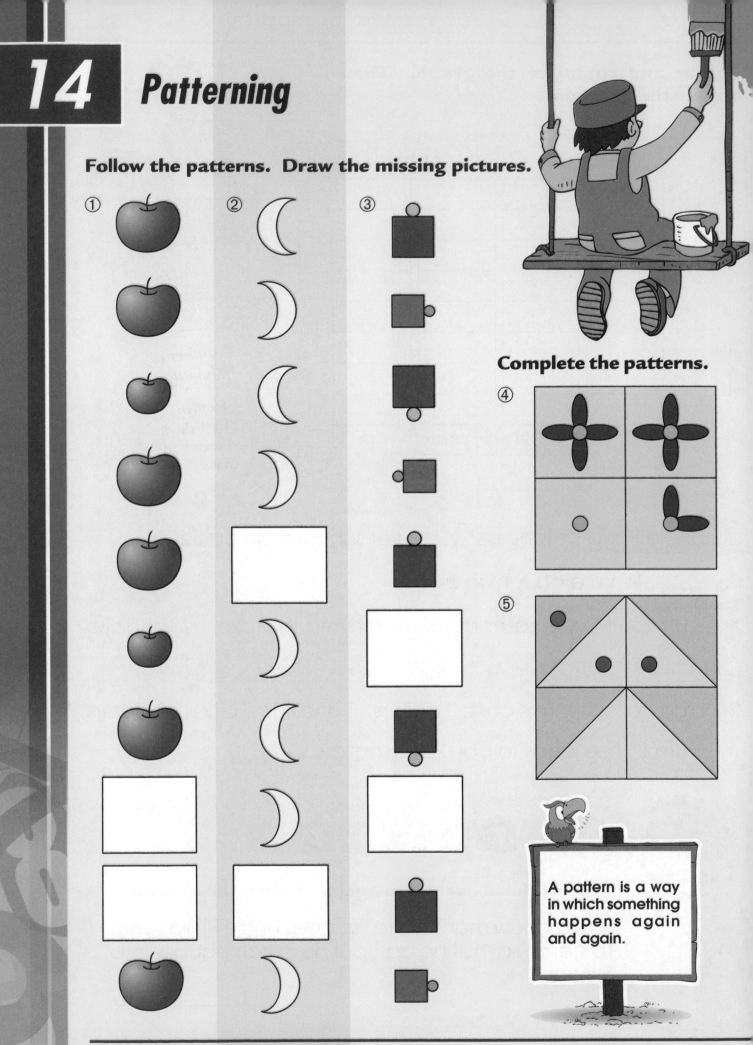

A pattern is a way in which something happens again and again.

ISBN: 978-1-927042-11-3

Look at the patterns. Then choose the correct words to describe the patterns.

colour   size   shape   position   orientation

⑥  By changing:

_____

⑦ 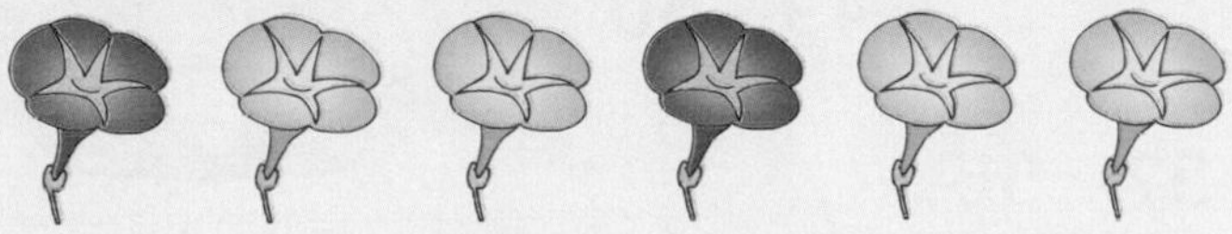 By changing:

_____

⑧  By changing:

_____ and _____

⑨  By changing:

_____ and _____

Look at each pattern and form a letter pattern with the same pattern rule. You may use any letters you like.

⑩

_____

⑪

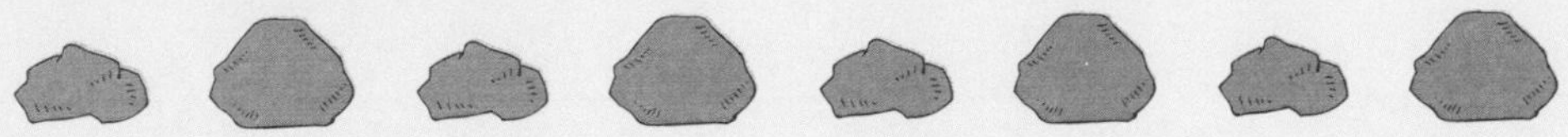

_____

ISBN: 978-1-927042-11-3

14

Complete the chart and answer the questions.

⑫

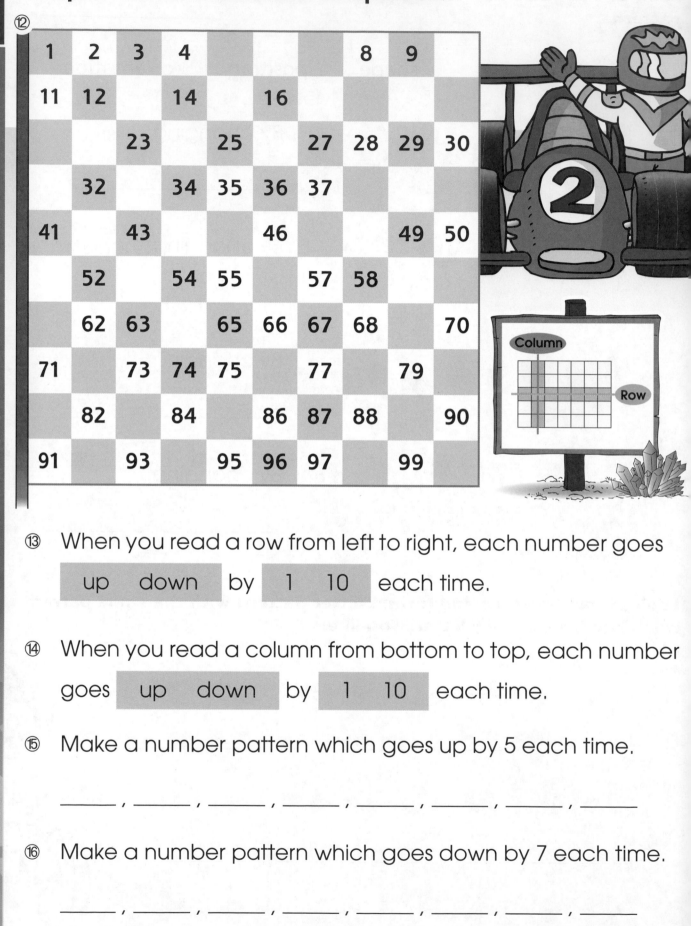

1	2	3	4				8	9	
11	12		14		16				
		23		25		27	28	29	30
	32		34	35	36	37			
41		43			46			49	50
	52		54	55		57	58		
	62	63		65	66	67	68		70
71		73	74	75		77		79	
	82		84		86	87	88		90
91		93		95	96	97		99	

Column

Row

⑬ When you read a row from left to right, each number goes

  up   down   by   1   10   each time.

⑭ When you read a column from bottom to top, each number

goes   up   down   by   1   10   each time.

⑮ Make a number pattern which goes up by 5 each time.

_____ , _____ , _____ , _____ , _____ , _____ , _____ , _____

⑯ Make a number pattern which goes down by 7 each time.

_____ , _____ , _____ , _____ , _____ , _____ , _____ , _____

Canadian Curriculum MathSmart (Grade 2)   ISBN: 978-1-927042-11-3

Follow each pattern to write the next 2 number sentences. Then write "Growing" or "Shrinking" to describe the pattern.

⑰ 32 + 2 = 34
34 + 2 = 36
36 + 2 = 38

_____
_____
• _____ pattern

⑱ 59 – 3 = 56
56 – 3 = 53
53 – 3 = 50

_____
_____
• _____ pattern

⑲ 90 – 10 = 80
90 – 20 = 70
90 – 30 = 60

_____
_____
• _____ pattern

⑳ 85 + 6 = 91
85 + 7 = 92
85 + 8 = 93

_____
_____
• _____ pattern

ACTIVITY

Follow each pattern to find the missing numbers with the help of a calculator.

① Multiply by 4: 1   4

② Divide by 2: 64   32

15 Transformation and Grid

	Flip	Slide	Turn
Flip :	5 ⟶ Ƨ		
Slide :	5 ⟶ 5		
Turn :	5 ⟶ upside 5		

Linda is playing a computer game. Help her circle ○ the correct words to describe the pictures.

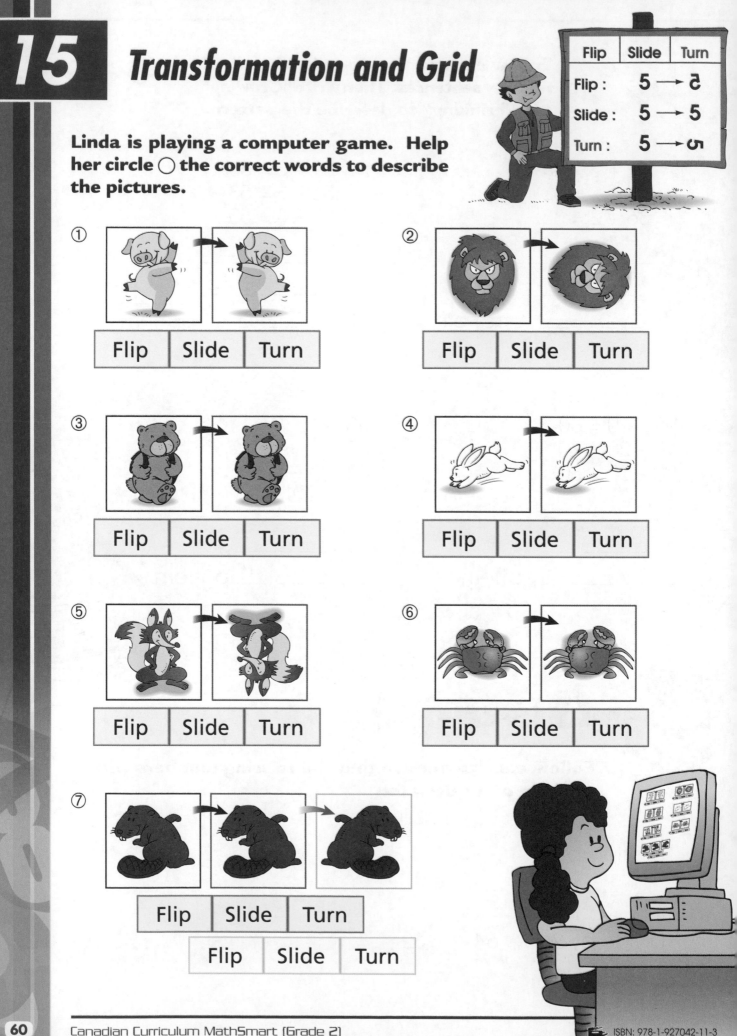

① Flip | Slide | Turn

② Flip | Slide | Turn

③ Flip | Slide | Turn

④ Flip | Slide | Turn

⑤ Flip | Slide | Turn

⑥ Flip | Slide | Turn

⑦ Flip | Slide | Turn

Flip | Slide | Turn

ISBN: 978-1-927042-11-3

Check ✔ the correct image for each transformation.

Flip
Slide
Turn

⑧ Turn (A) (B) (C)

⑨ Flip (A) (B) (C)

⑩ Slide (A) (B) (C)

Draw the images.

⑪ Flip image of ▢ .

⑫ Turn image of ▲ .

⑬ Flip image of 🏠 .

⑭ Turn image of 🏠 .

⑮ Slide image of ▢ .

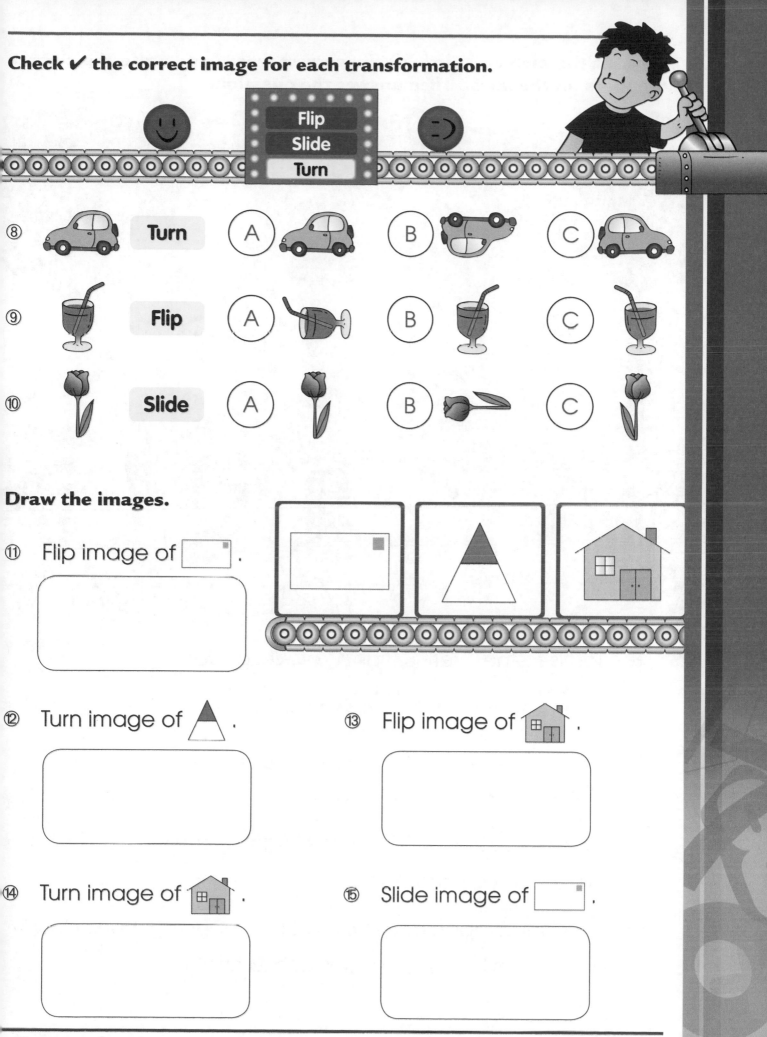

ISBN: 978-1-927042-11-3

Look at the picture. Circle ◯ the correct words and write the correct numbers on the lines. Then answer the question.

Mabel is on my left.

⑯ Joe is to the [left right] of Alexander.

⑰ Kevin is to the [left right] of Sue.

⑱ John is ____ unit(s) [left right] and ____ unit(s) [up down] from Anita.

⑲ Tina is ____ unit(s) [left right] and ____ unit(s) [up down] from Joe.

⑳ Michael swaps places with a child by going 1 unit down and 2 units left. Who swaps with Michael?

_____

ISBN: 978-1-927042-11-3

Help Ron draw and colour the shapes.

㉑ Draw a ■ 2 units to the right and 4 units down from the ★ .

㉒ Draw a ⬡ 1 unit to the left and 1 unit up from the ● .

㉓ Draw a ⬠ 4 units down and 3 units left of the ▲ .

A C T I V I T Y

Put a mirror along the dotted line. Then draw the clock hands on the right to show the flip image.

Probability

Michelle is going to pick a flower from the vase. Look at the flowers. Help Michelle solve the problems.

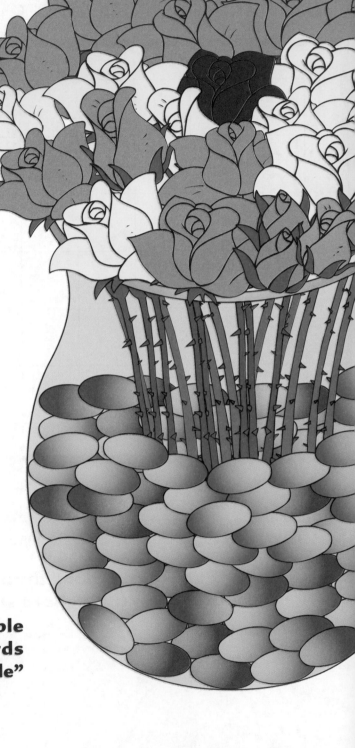

① Is there any chance of picking a sunflower?

_____

② Is it unlikely to pick a yellow rose?

_____

③ Is it unlikely to pick a red rose?

_____

④ Is it possible to pick a purple rose?

_____

Michelle wants to pick a pebble from the vase. Use the words "likely", "unlikely", or "impossible" to describe the chances.

⑤ The chance of picking a

   a. blue pebble _____

   b. red pebble _____

   c. yellow pebble _____

   d. green pebble _____

ISBN: 978-1-927042-11-3

You can get the thing that you point at.

The children are playing a spinning game. Help them solve the problems.

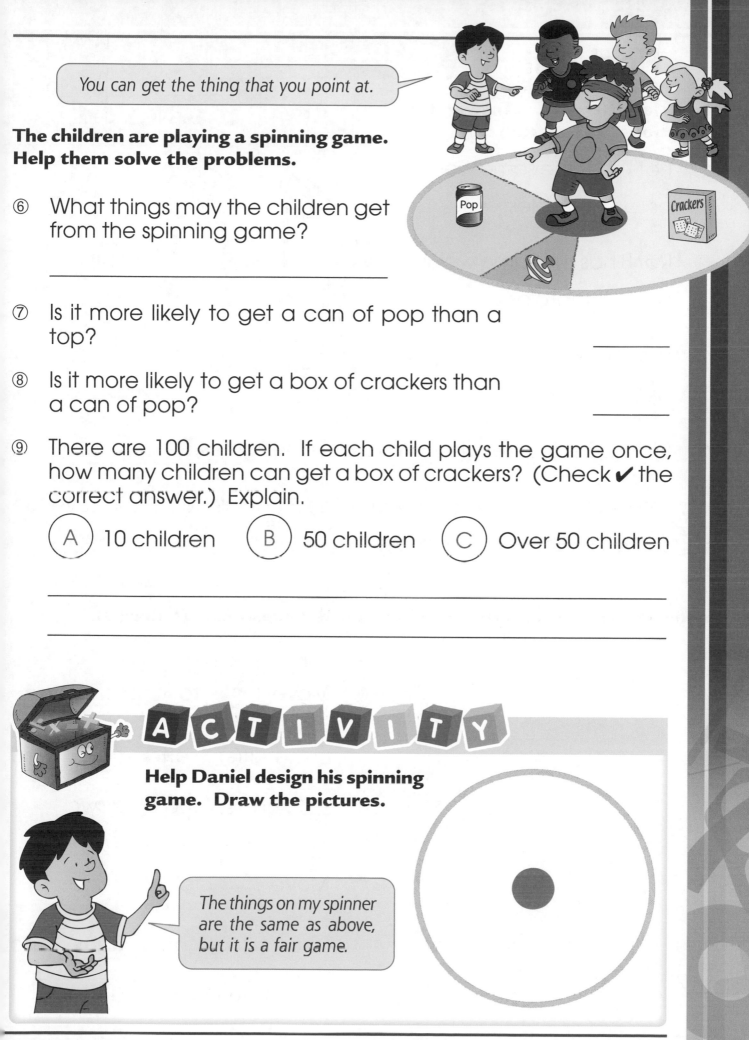

⑥ What things may the children get from the spinning game?

_____

⑦ Is it more likely to get a can of pop than a top?

_____

⑧ Is it more likely to get a box of crackers than a can of pop?

_____

⑨ There are 100 children. If each child plays the game once, how many children can get a box of crackers? (Check ✔ the correct answer.) Explain.

  Ⓐ 10 children   Ⓑ 50 children   Ⓒ Over 50 children

_____

_____

ACTIVITY

Help Daniel design his spinning game. Draw the pictures.

The things on my spinner are the same as above, but it is a fair game.

Final Test

Look at the rats. Answer the questions. (12 marks)

① Rat A has the same weight as ____ marbles.

② Rat B has the same weight as ____ marbles.

③ Rat C has the same weight as ____ marbles.

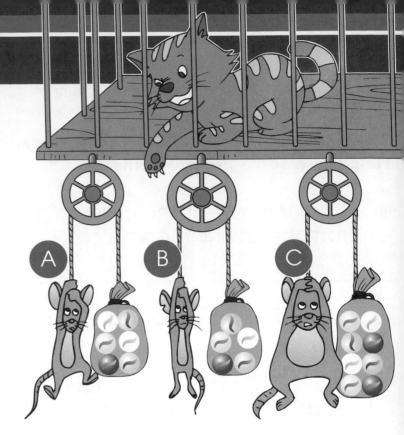

④ Rat ____ is the heaviest. Rat ____ is the lightest.

⑤ If a marble has the same weight as 2 pencils, Rat B will have the same weight as ____ pencils.

Look at the things on the floor. Answer the questions. (8 marks)

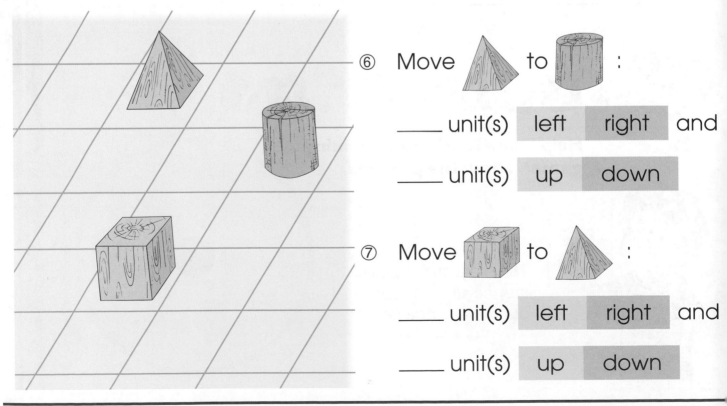

⑥ Move △ to ⬤ :

____ unit(s) | left | right | and

____ unit(s) | up | down

⑦ Move ⬛ to △ :

____ unit(s) | left | right | and

____ unit(s) | up | down

ISBN: 978-1-927042-11-3

Find the answers. (14 marks)

⑧
$$\begin{array}{r} 27 \\ + 17 \\ \hline \end{array}$$

⑨
$$\begin{array}{r} 39 \\ + 25 \\ \hline \end{array}$$

⑩
$$\begin{array}{r} 90 \\ - 46 \\ \hline \end{array}$$

⑪
$$\begin{array}{r} 82 \\ - 53 \\ \hline \end{array}$$

⑫
$$\begin{array}{r} 5 \\ \times \quad 5 \\ \hline \end{array}$$

⑬
$$\begin{array}{r} 3 \\ \times \quad 7 \\ \hline \end{array}$$

⑭
$$\begin{array}{r} 9 \\ \times \quad 6 \\ \hline \end{array}$$

⑮
$$\begin{array}{r} 4 \\ \times \quad 8 \\ \hline \end{array}$$

⑯ $82 - 28 =$ _____

⑰ $8 \times 8 =$ _____

⑱ $49 + 33 =$ _____

⑲ $2 \times 4 =$ _____

⑳ $90 - 35 =$ _____

㉑ $7 \times 9 =$ _____

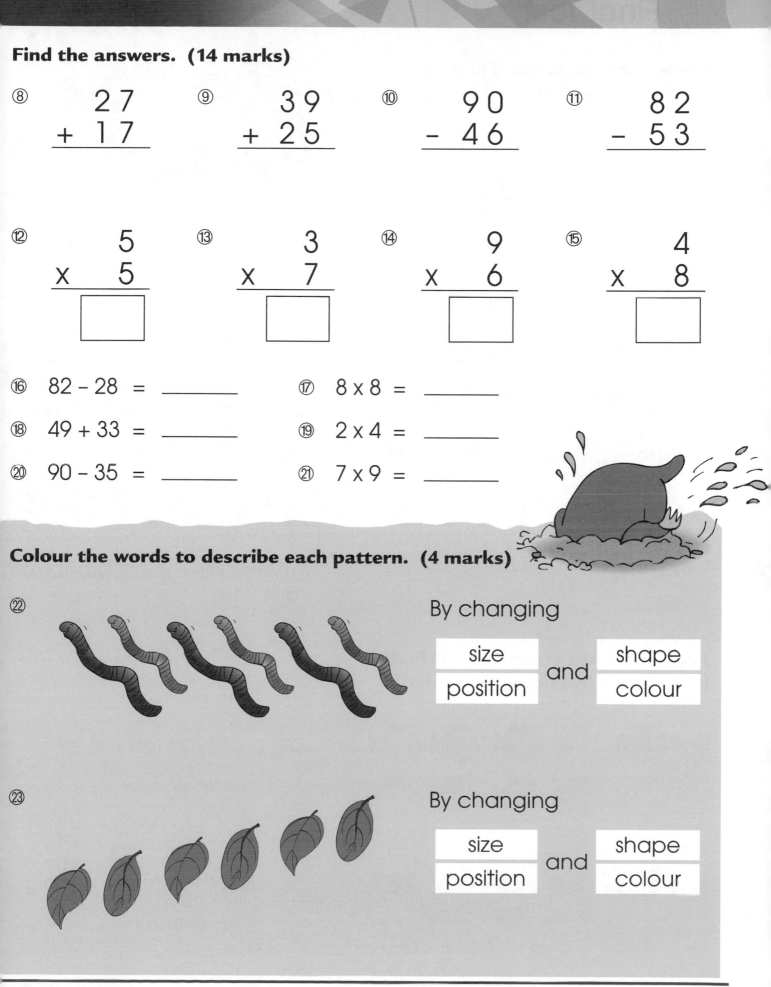

Colour the words to describe each pattern. (4 marks)

㉒ By changing

size		shape
position	and	colour

㉓ By changing

size		shape
position	and	colour

ISBN: 978-1-927042-11-3

Final Test

Circle ◯ the pictures. Fill in the blanks. (6 marks)

㉔ There are 4 🐚 in a group.

Circle ◯ every 4 🐚 .

There are _____ groups of 4 in 20.

㉕ There are 6 🐚 in a group.

Circle ◯ every 6 🐚 .

There are _____ groups of 6 in 24.

Look at the sea creatures. Fill in the blanks with fractions. (4 marks)

㉖ _____ of the fish are red;

_____ are yellow.

㉗ _____ of the crabs are big;

_____ are small.

ISBN: 978-1-927042-11-3

Look at Judy's mobile. Help her colour the graph. Then answer the questions. (8 marks)

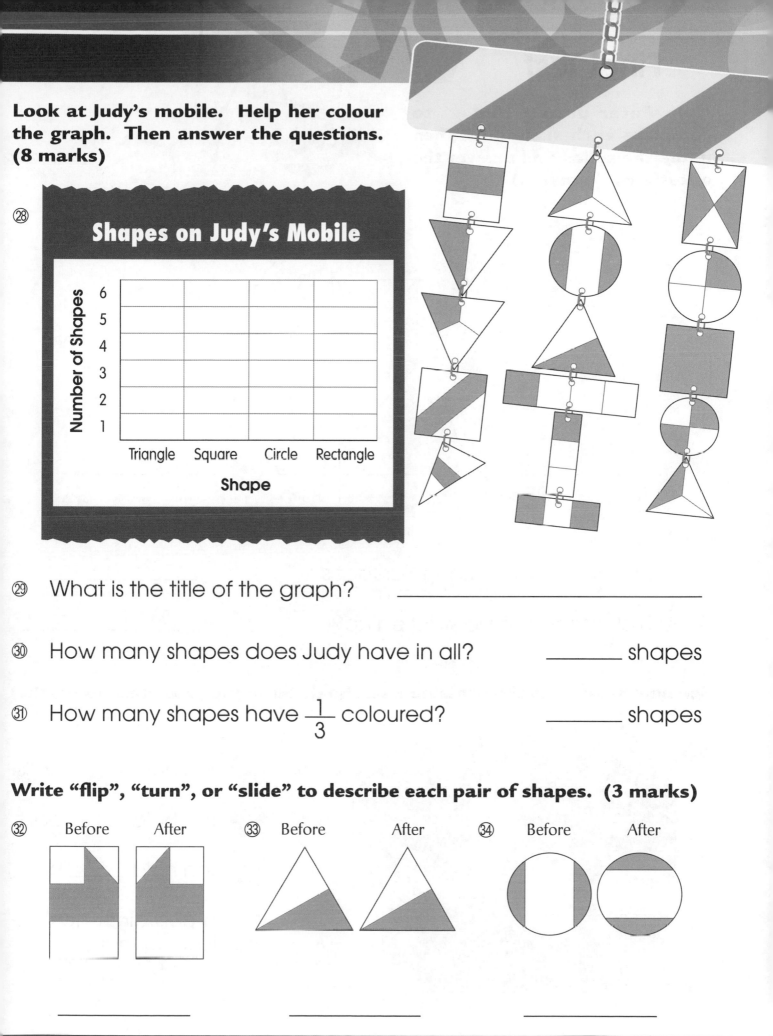

㉘ **Shapes on Judy's Mobile**

Number of Shapes

6
5
4
3
2
1

Triangle   Square   Circle   Rectangle

Shape

㉙ What is the title of the graph? _____

㉚ How many shapes does Judy have in all? _____ shapes

㉛ How many shapes have $\frac{1}{3}$ coloured? _____ shapes

Write "flip", "turn", or "slide" to describe each pair of shapes. (3 marks)

㉜ Before   After   ㉝ Before   After   ㉞ Before   After

_____   _____   _____

Final Test

Help Peter draw • and ╱ to complete each skeleton. Then name the solids and answer the questions. (8 marks)

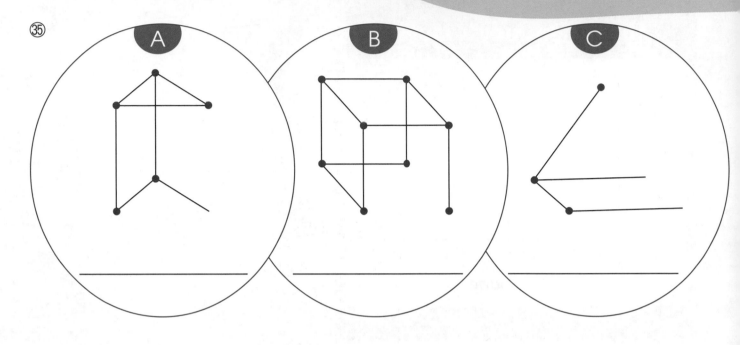

㉟

A _____

B _____

C _____

㊱ Which solids have triangular faces? _____

㊲ Which solids can be stacked up? _____

See how many balls the containers can hold. Solve the problems. (8 marks)

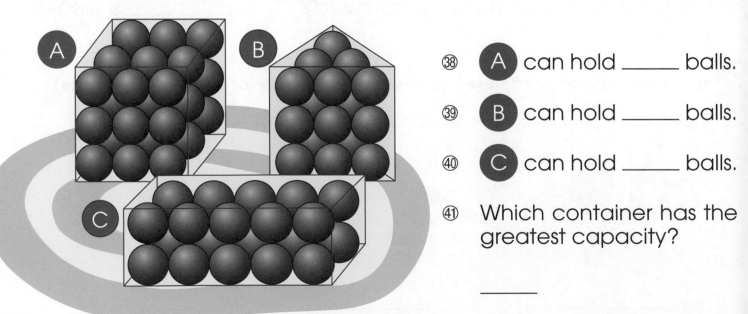

㊳ A can hold ____ balls.

㊴ B can hold ____ balls.

㊵ C can hold ____ balls.

㊶ Which container has the greatest capacity?

____

ISBN: 978-1-927042-11-3

Follow each pattern to write the next 2 numbers. Then circle ⃝ the correct word and fill in the blank. (8 marks)

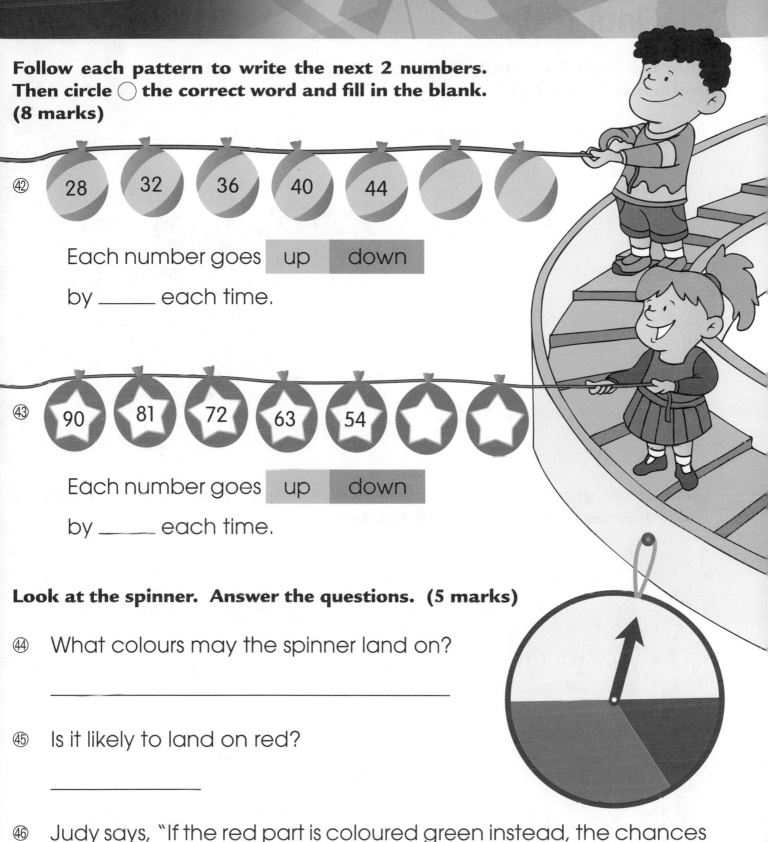

42 28 32 36 40 44 ___ ___

Each number goes   up   down

by ___ each time.

43 90 81 72 63 54 ___ ___

Each number goes   up   down

by ___ each time.

Look at the spinner. Answer the questions. (5 marks)

44 What colours may the spinner land on?

_____

45 Is it likely to land on red?

_____

46 Judy says, "If the red part is coloured green instead, the chances of the spinner landing on yellow and green will be the same." Is she correct? Explain.

_____

_____

Final Test

Aunt Eva has a fruit stall. Help her solve the problems. (6 marks)

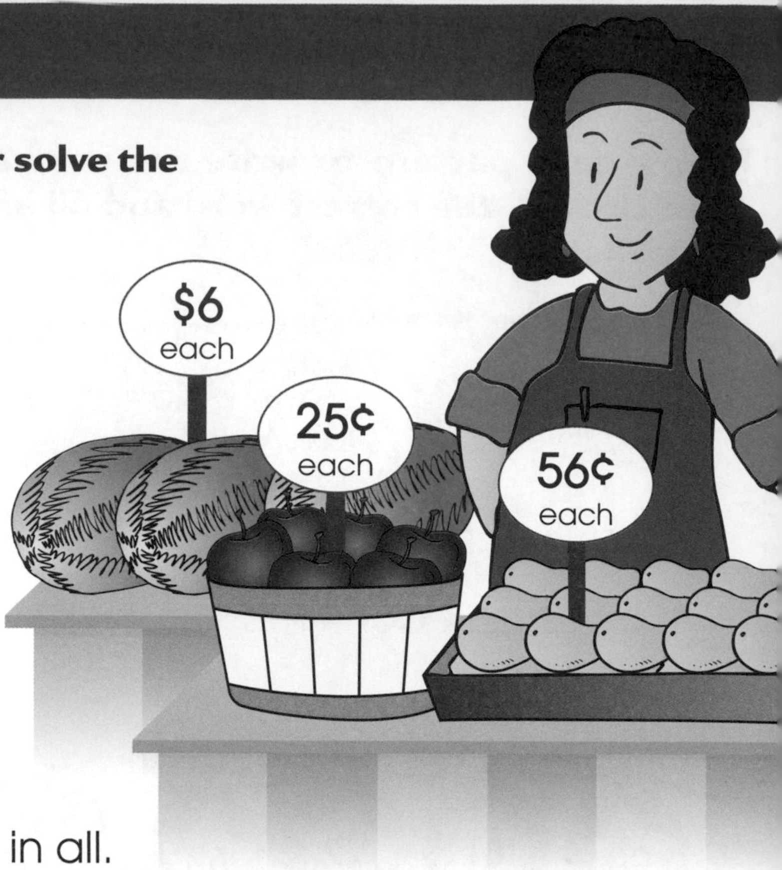
$6
each
25¢
each
56¢
each

㊼ If Mrs. Spencer buys an apple with 30¢, her change will be ______ ¢.

㊽ An orange costs 38¢ less than a mango. An orange costs ______ ¢.

㊾ 7 watermelons cost $ ______ in all.

Look at the graph to see how many apples weigh the same as each kind of fruit. Answer the questions. (6 marks)

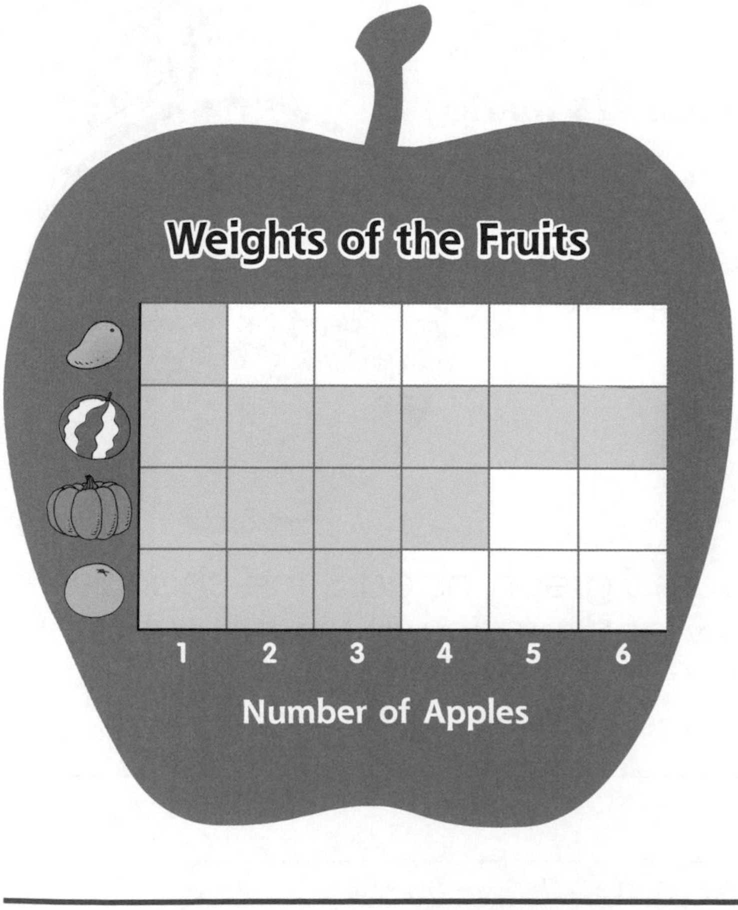
Weights of the Fruits
1 2 3 4 5 6
Number of Apples

㊿ ______ apples are needed to balance 1 watermelon.

(51) ______ mangoes are needed to balance 1 pumpkin.

(52) ______ melons are needed to balance 1 watermelon.

Score

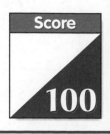

100

ISBN: 978-1-927042-11-3

1 Numbers to 100

1. Nine
2. Thirteen
3. Seventeen
4. Fifteen
5. Twenty
6. 68 ; 70 ; 71
7. 86 ; 84 ; 83
8. 40 ; 42 ; 45
9. 91 ; 89 ; 86
10. 20
11. 40
12. 50
13. 12
14. 18, 32, 39
15. 20, 56, 75
16. 29, 40, 92
17. 25
18. 39
19. 45
20. 82
21. 91
22. 67
23. 70
24. 3
25. 3 ; 8
26. 5 ; 4
27. 7 ; 5
28. 4 ; 2
29. 8 ; 6
30. 2
31. 89, 90, 91
32. (Suggested answer) 90, 92
33. 87
34. 88
35.

36. red
37. 4th ; 16th
38. 7

Activity

1. 32 ; 21
2. 73

2 Addition

1. 17
2. 18
3. 16
4. 18
5. 18
6. 16
7. 19
8. 19
9. 19
10. 14
11. 16
12. 17
13. 19
14. 15 ; 4 ; 19 ;

```
  1 5
+   4
  1 9
```

15. 6 ; 12 ; 18 ;

```
    6
+ 1 2
  1 8
```

16. tens 5 ones 13 ; 63 ;

```
    ①
  3 4
+ 2 9
  6 3
```

17. tens 3 ones 10 ; 40 ;

```
    ①
  2 2
+ 1 8
  4 0
```

18. tens 2 ones 11 ; 31 ;

```
    ①
  1 4
+ 1 7
  3 1
```

19. 26
20. 41
21. 44
22. 83
23. 40
24. 89
25. 68
26. 86
27. 80
28. 80
29. 52
30. 73
31. 51
32. 54
33. 76
34. 54
35. 70
36. 22 ; 19 ; 41 ; 41
37. 48 ; 38 ; 86 ; 86
38. 17 ; 16 ; 33 ; 33

Activity

B

3 Subtraction

1. 9 ; 4 ; 5
2. 16 ; 9 ; 7
3. 5
4. 8
5. 8
6. 5
7. 8
8. 3
9. 7
10. 9
11. 3
12. 8
13. 3
14. 7
15. 1
16. 7
17. 6
18. 6
19. 14
20. 33
21. 18
22. 48
23. 61
24. 24
25. 31
26. 2
27. 24
28. 4
29. 36
30. 28
31. 34
32. 29
33. 25
34. 27 ;

```
  4 1
- 1 4
  2 7
```

35. 7 ;

```
  2 2
- 1 5
    7
```

36a. 35 ; 16 ; 19 ; 19
b. 19 ; 16 ; 3 ; 3

37. Peter   38. 8
39. 17
40a. 19   b. 54

Activity

9

4 More about Addition and Subtraction

1. 45 ; 26 ; 71 ;   2. 39 ; 45 ; 84
   71 ; 26 ; 45   84 ; 45 ; 39
3. 16 ; 36 ; 52 ;   4. 13 ; 68 ; 81
   52 ; 36 ; 16   81 ; 68 ; 13
5. 21 ; 21   6. 51 ; 51
7. 42 ; 42   8. 72 ; 72
9. 74   10. 36
11. 18   12. 93
13. 69   14. 99
15. 36   16. 34
17. 18   18. 53
19. 16   20. 25
21. 90   22. 14
23. 71   24. 54
25. 39   26. 39 ; + ; 33 ; 72 ; 72
27. 41 ; − ; 28 ; 13 ; 13   28. 24 ; − ; 16 ; 8 ; 8
29a. 19 ; + ; 17 ; 36 ; 36   b. 36 ; − ; 9 ; 27 ; 27
30. 43 ; 18   31. 51 ; 67
32. 15 ; 23   33. 84
34. 18   35. 37
36. 38   37. 36

Activity

1. 10   2. 19
3. 61   4. 54

5 Time and Temperature

1. March ; April ; June ; September ; November
2. 12   3. June
4. Saturday   5. 31
6. 19   7. August
8. August 1   9. July 9 ; Saturday
10.   ; 02:50 ; 3

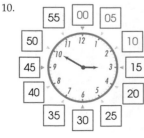

11. 06:55 ; 7   12. 09:20 ; 9
13. 01:10 ; 10 ; 1   14. 11:50 ; 10 ; 12
15. 15   16. 45
17. 1 ; 15   18. A : 20 ; B : 5
19. B   20. down
21. up   22. likely
23. unlikely   24. unlikely
25. likely

Activity

6:45

6 Length, Perimeter, and Area

1. ✔   2. ✘
3. ✘   4. ✘
5. ✔
6.

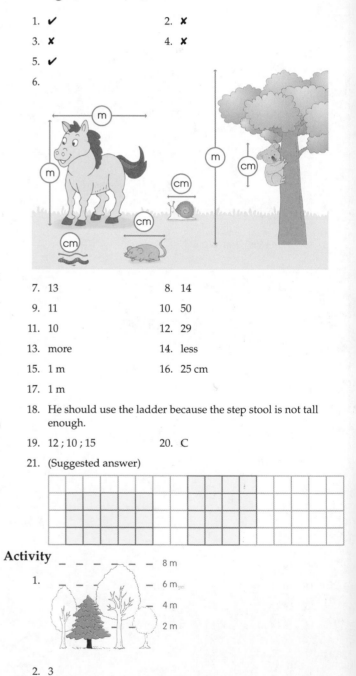

7. 13   8. 14
9. 11   10. 50
11. 10   12. 29
13. more   14. less
15. 1 m   16. 25 cm
17. 1 m
18. He should use the ladder because the step stool is not tall enough.
19. 12 ; 10 ; 15   20. C
21. (Suggested answer)

Activity

1.
— 8 m
— 6 m
— 4 m
— 2 m

2. 3

ISBN: 978-1-927042-11-3

7 Money

1. Dime ; 10¢
2. Penny ; 1¢
3. Quarter ; 25¢
4. Nickel ; 5¢
5. Toonie ; $2
6. Loonie ; $1
7. A : 100¢ or $1   B : 86¢
   C : 89¢
8. A
9.

10. The bear
11. The giraffe
12. 2
13. 42
14.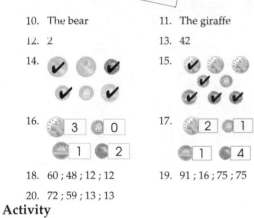
15.
16. 3 0
    1 2
17. 2 1
    1 4
18. 60 ; 48 ; 12 ; 12
19. 91 ; 16 ; 75 ; 75
20. 72 ; 59 ; 13 ; 13

Activity
C ; D ; E

8 Shapes

1. Triangle ; Pentagon ; Rectangle ; Square ; Hexagon ; Octagon
2. ; 6 ; 6
3. ; 8 ; 8
4. 3 ; 3
5. 4 ; 4
6. pentagon
7. octagon
8. Hexagon, Triangle
9. Octagon, Square
10. Square, Rectangle

---

11. C
12. B
13. A
14. C
15. A
16. B
17.
18.
19.
20.

Activity
1. 1
2. 5
3. 7
4. 9

Midway Test

1. 14 : Fourteen   11 : Eleven
   17 : Seventeen   19 : Nineteen
   20 : Twenty   15 : Fifteen
2. 71, 62, 57
3. 62, 54, 45
4. 79 ; 80 ; 82
5. 88 ; 84 ; 82
6. 37
7. 54
8. 62
9. 17
10. 62
11. 80
12. 51
13. 93
14. 29
15. 70
16. 56
17. 27
18. A : Triangle   B : Hexagon
    C : Rectangle   D : Square
    E : Pentagon   F : Octagon
19. 6 ; 6
20. 5 ; 5
21. No
22. B
23. C
24. 6
25. A : 2   B : 3
    C : 4
26a. 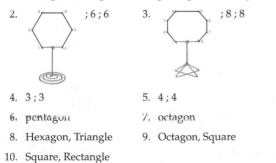 ; 18   b. ; 19
27. 57 ; 36
28. No
29. 43
30. 72
31. 62
32a. 58   b. 77

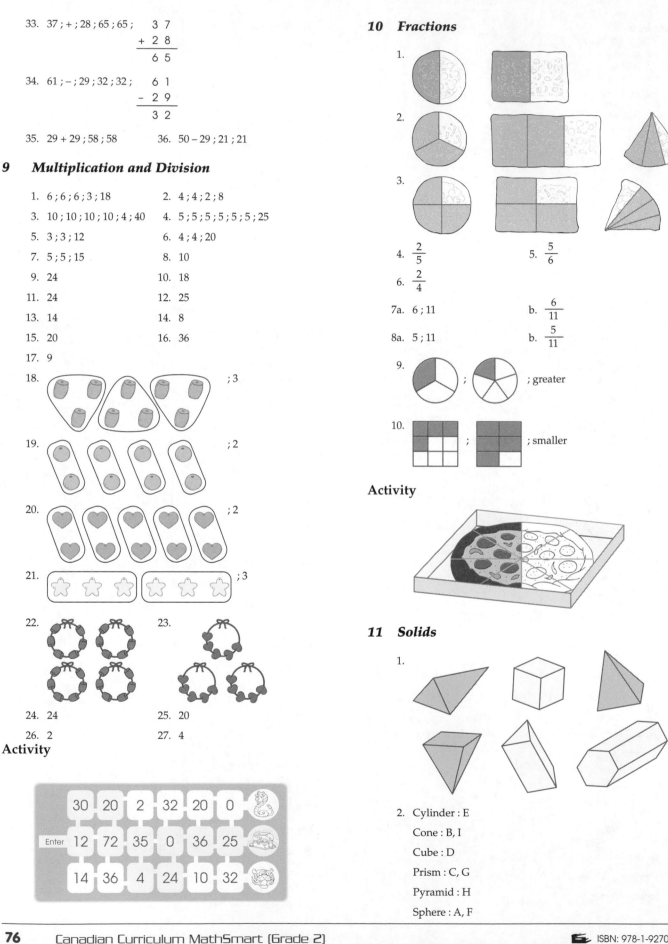

33. 37 ; + ; 28 ; 65 ; 65 ;

$$\begin{array}{r} 3\ 7 \\ +\ 2\ 8 \\ \hline 6\ 5 \end{array}$$

34. 61 ; − ; 29 ; 32 ; 32 ;

$$\begin{array}{r} 6\ 1 \\ -\ 2\ 9 \\ \hline 3\ 2 \end{array}$$

35. 29 + 29 ; 58 ; 58   36. 50 − 29 ; 21 ; 21

9 Multiplication and Division

1. 6 ; 6 ; 6 ; 3 ; 18   2. 4 ; 4 ; 2 ; 8
3. 10 ; 10 ; 10 ; 10 ; 4 ; 40   4. 5 ; 5 ; 5 ; 5 ; 5 ; 5 ; 25
5. 3 ; 3 ; 12   6. 4 ; 4 ; 20
7. 5 ; 5 ; 15   8. 10
9. 24   10. 18
11. 24   12. 25
13. 14   14. 8
15. 20   16. 36
17. 9
18.   ; 3
19.   ; 2
20.   ; 2
21.   ; 3
22.   23.
24. 24   25. 20
26. 2   27. 4

Activity

10 Fractions

1.
2.
3.
4. $\frac{2}{5}$ 5. $\frac{5}{6}$
6. $\frac{2}{4}$
7a. 6 ; 11   b. $\frac{6}{11}$
8a. 5 ; 11   b. $\frac{5}{11}$
9.   ;   ; greater
10.   ;   ; smaller

Activity

11 Solids

1.
2. Cylinder : E
   Cone : B, I
   Cube : D
   Prism : C, G
   Pyramid : H
   Sphere : A, F

ISBN: 978-1-927042-11-3

3. A, B, E, F, and I

4. B, C, D, E, G, H, and I

5. C, D, E, and G

6. B, E, and I

7.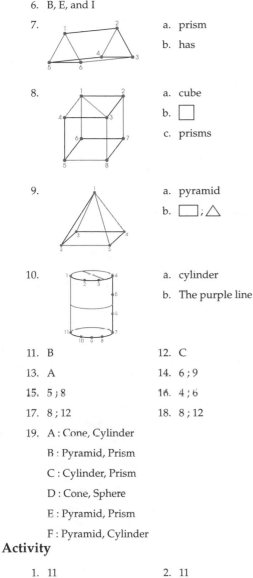
   a. prism
   b. has

8.
   a. cube
   b. □
   c. prisms

9.
   a. pyramid
   b. □ ; △

10.
   a. cylinder
   b. The purple line

11. B   12. C

13. A   14. 6 ; 9

15. 5 ; 8   16. 4 ; 6

17. 8 ; 12   18. 8 ; 12

19. A : Cone, Cylinder

    B : Pyramid, Prism

    C : Cylinder, Prism

    D : Cone, Sphere

    E : Pyramid, Prism

    F : Pyramid, Cylinder

Activity

1. 11   2. 11

12 Capacity and Mass

1. lighter ; heavier   2. 20

3. 5   4. 5

5.   6.

7. 2   8. 10

9. 3   10. 10

11. 6   12.

13. 2   14. 3 ; 1 ; 2

Activity

20

13 Graphs

1.

Children's Favourite Animals

No. of Children	Lion	Giraffe	Hippo	Monkey	Tiger
6			🍌		
5		🦒	🍌	🐵	
4	🦁	🦒	🍌	🐵	
3	🦁	🦒	🍌	🐵	
2	🦁	🦒	🍌	🐵	🐯
1	🦁	🦒	🍌	🐵	🐯

Animal

2. 5   3. 4

4. 4   5. Hippo

6. Tiger   7. 22

8. 10   9. Days of Sunshine

10. July, August, and September

11. 16   12. 8

13. 34   14. 18

15.

No. of Boxes of Ice Cream

Number of Boxes	Vanilla	Strawberry	Chocolate	Neapolitan
6				
5				
4				
3				
2				
1				

Ice Cream

16. 5   17. 4

18. 18   19. 6

20. 14

21. Vanilla : 18   Strawberry : 30

    Chocolate : 36   Neapolitan : 24

ISBN: 970-1-927042-11-3

22.

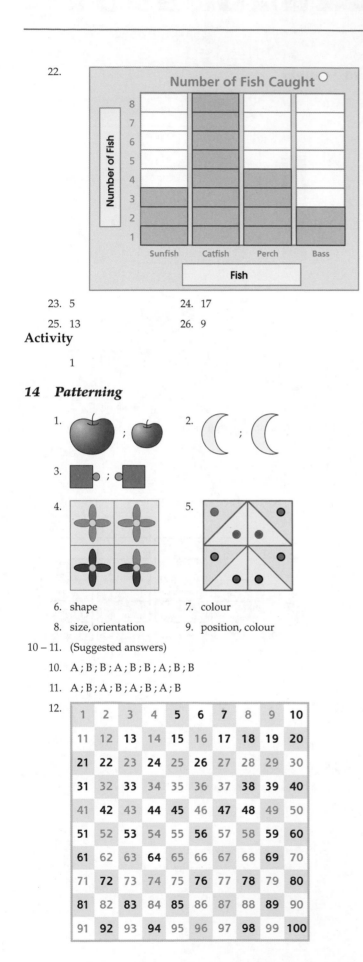

Number of Fish Caught

23. 5   24. 17

25. 13   26. 9

Activity

1

14 Patterning

1.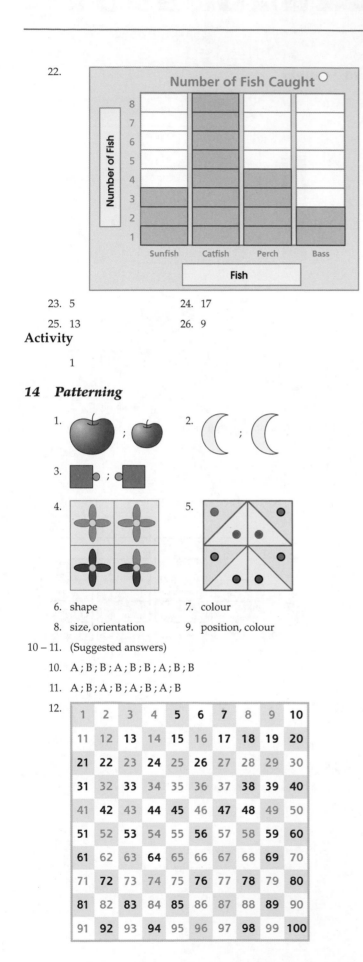

2.

3.

4.

5.

6. shape   7. colour

8. size, orientation   9. position, colour

10 – 11. (Suggested answers)

10. A ; B ; B ; A ; B ; B ; A ; B ; B

11. A ; B ; A ; B ; A ; B ; A ; B

12.

1	2	3	4	5	6	7	8	9	10
11	12	13	14	15	16	17	18	19	20
21	22	23	24	25	26	27	28	29	30
31	32	33	34	35	36	37	38	39	40
41	42	43	44	45	46	47	48	49	50
51	52	53	54	55	56	57	58	59	60
61	62	63	64	65	66	67	68	69	70
71	72	73	74	75	76	77	78	79	80
81	82	83	84	85	86	87	88	89	90
91	92	93	94	95	96	97	98	99	100

13. up ; 1   14. down ; 10

15 – 16. (Suggested answers)

15. 5 ; 10 ; 15 ; 20 ; 25 ; 30 ; 35 ; 40

16. 7 ; 14 ; 21 ; 28 ; 35 ; 42 ; 49 ; 56

17. 38 + 2 = 40 ;   18. 50 – 3 = 47 ;

     40 + 2 = 42 ;   47 – 3 = 44 ;

     Growing   Shrinking

19. 90 – 40 = 50 ;   20. 85 + 9 = 94 ;

     90 – 50 = 40 ;   85 + 10 = 95 ;

     Shrinking   Growing

Activity

1. 16 ; 64 ; 256 ; 1024

2. 16 ; 8 ; 4 ; 2

15 Transformation and Grid

1. Flip   2. Turn

3. Slide   4. Slide

5. Turn   6. Flip

7. Slide ; Flip   8. B

9. C   10. A

11.   12.

13.   14.

15.

16. right   17. left

18. 3 ; right ; 1 ; up   19. 2 ; left ; 2 ; up

20. Anita

21 – 23.

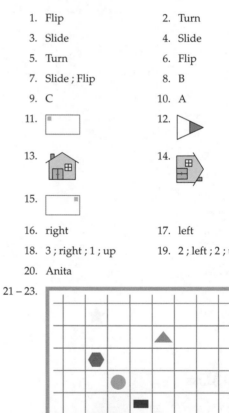

Activity

ISBN: 978-1-927042-11-3

16 Probability

1. No
2. No
3. Yes
4. No
5a. unlikely
b. impossible
c. impossible
d. likely
6. A can of pop, a top, or a box of crackers
7. Yes
8. Yes
9. C ; The part with the box of crackers covers more than half of the spinner.

Activity

Final Test

1. 6
2. 5
3. 8
4. C ; B
5. 10
6. 2 ; right ; 1 ; down
7. 1 ; left ; 3 ; up
8. 44
9. 64
10. 44
11. 29
12. 25
13. 21
14. 54
15. 32
16. 54
17. 64
18. 82
19. 8
20. 55
21. 63
22. size ; colour
23. position ; shape
24. 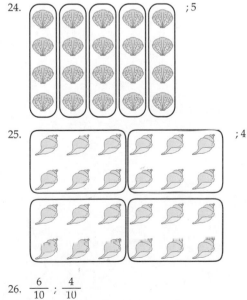 ; 5

25.  ; 4

26. $\frac{6}{10}$; $\frac{4}{10}$

27. $\frac{3}{12}$; $\frac{9}{12}$

28.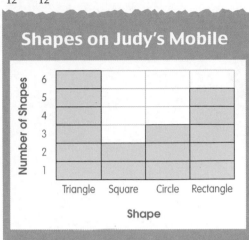
Shapes on Judy's Mobile

29. Shapes on Judy's Mobile
30. 16
31. 5
32. flip
33. slide
34. turn
35.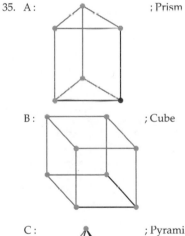
A : ; Prism
B : ; Cube
C : ; Pyramid

36. A and C
37. A and B
38. 27
39. 18
40. 20
41. A
42. 48 ; 52 ; up ; 4
43. 45 ; 36 ; down ; 9
44. Yellow, green, or red
45. No
46. Yes, because the yellow part will have the same size as the green part.
47. 5
48. 18
49. 42
50. 6
51. 4
52. 2

ISBN: 978-1-927042-11-3